About Quicklook at Vets

MILLIONS of us care for animals. Man's relationship with them is varied and complex. The work of vets reflects this and covers an enormous number of species.

Quicklook at Vets provides a fascinating insight into how vets do their work and the astonishing way in which this is developing. All main aspects are covered, from small family pets to farm animals and (sometimes very valuable) horses.

Find out what vets and veterinary nurses have to do to qualify. Get under the skin of a working practice. See what it does and how it is organised. What treatments are available? Are they affordable and justified?

What is the future of this fast evolving profession, which is so vital to our connection with the animal world?

Quicklook at
Vets

Bob Lehner

Quicklook
books

Published by Quicklook Books Limited

Weighbridge House, Grittleton SN14 6AP

First edition in e-book format 2011

This revised edition first published in hard copy 2012

Copyright Quicklook Books Limited (Company number 06641038) 2012

Cover photo from istockphoto.com

Books in the Quicklook series are available in hard copy and as e-books from www.quicklookbooks.com

Contact info@quicklookbooks.com

Printed and bound by CPI Group (UK) Ltd, Croydon, CR0 4YY

Quicklook is a registered European trade mark (number 008147258)

ISBN 978-1-908926-01-2

Contents

Chapter One
Man and animals

Our association with, and exploitation of, animals extends as far back as human history itself. No matter how urbanised, or cut off from nature people become, they still retain their desire to share their lives with animals.

We have always kept and used animals for many different purposes. These include those historically reared for food or clothing, those used for transportation, to serve as beasts of burden, or to provide a source of power in agriculture. Others are kept for sporting and recreational purposes. Dogs are kept to guard us, or to work for us in other ways, whilst some animals are kept solely to be our companions.

Within these broad categories there is a wide range of species. For example, animals raised for food production across the world include cattle, sheep, pigs, horses, goats, reindeer, llamas, camels, buffalo, dogs, rabbits, guinea pigs, poultry and fish. Those used for transportation and agriculture include horses, donkeys, cattle, camels, buffalo, yaks and llamas. Horses, camels, dogs and birds are kept for sporting purposes, whilst those with a role as companions range from dogs, cats, rabbits and guinea pigs through to all manner of birds and reptiles.

It is interesting to note how different cultures make use of different species for these various purposes. Eating one kind of animal may be considered normal in one culture, but totally abhorrent in another, No self-respecting Englishman would even consider eating a dog, whereas this is quite acceptable in some Oriental countries. The Western tendency to share one's house, or even one's bed, with a dog would be considered quite inappropriate by many people from the Middle East.

The ever-expanding human population places more and more demands on food production. Whilst it is clear that mankind could exist quite satisfactorily on a vegetarian diet, it is striking that as previously poor countries, such as India and China, achieve greater affluence, one of the first thing their citizens want is an increased amount of meat in the diet. Thus livestock production is likely to be a high priority and will become more intensive and industrialised in areas of the world where it was previously conducted at a relatively low level.

In the West we now rather discount the use of animals for transportation and as a source of power in agriculture. However in many parts of the world horses, donkeys and draught cattle play a vital part in day-to-day life. Although these animals are very valuable to their owners, their health and welfare is often poor, largely due to the poverty and ignorance of the owners.

In our own society horses are now used almost entirely for recreational and sporting purposes and have been elevated to the same high status as our smaller pets. In many cases they lead a very privileged and cosseted lifestyle.

The role of animals as companions to humans is fascinating. In the Western world particularly, dogs and cats are often treated as one of the family and lavishly provided for. A recent survey suggests that there are some 10.5 million dogs and only slightly fewer cats in the UK and that 31% of households own dogs as compared to 26% with cats. Huge amounts of money are devoted to feeding them and tending to all their needs. This extends to their healthcare and as we shall see later, in some cases this can far exceed that available to many people in poorer parts of the world.

However, even though we are considered to be a nation of "animal lovers", it is not all "good news" for pets in our country. In 2008-9 it was estimated that over 9,000 homeless dogs were euthanased in the UK, whilst Battersea Dogs' Home in London took in over 11,000 lost, stray or unwanted animals.

It is interesting to note however, that even in impoverished third-world countries, dogs and cats often share their lives with humans, although economic factors limit the resources devoted to them.

In recent years the plight of the world's wildlife has come under increasing scrutiny. Expanding human populations in many parts of the world have squeezed wild animals into smaller and smaller habitats, such that their very survival is often threatened. Over-exploitation of species used for food, or poaching, has led to a vast reduction in numbers, or even extinction in some cases. Man-made pollution has wiped out other species.

The competition for resources between humans and wild animals means that many are facing extinction and their only hope of survival is either within strict conservation areas or alternatively in zoos.

The veterinary profession plays a vital role in all these areas, wherever the lives of humans and animals interact.

Chapter Two
What is veterinary medicine?

VETERINARY medicine is the branch of medical science that applies to all animals other than the human species, responsibility for which is the preserve of the human medical profession. It is concerned with the study of the whole spectrum of diseases affecting animals, caused by whatever means and their diagnosis, treatment and prevention. This is clearly a truly massive remit and therefore veterinary medicine mainly concentrates on those species of most direct importance to mankind.

"Disease" is any condition or process that adversely affects the normal physiological functions of all, or a part, of the body. Diseases are caused by exposure to harmful external or internal agents or factors.

External causes of disease include exposure to poisons and toxins, infection by viruses, bacteria or parasites, lack (or an excess) of food or essential food components such as vitamins and minerals, a lack of water or oxygen, exposure to extremes of temperature, radiation or trauma.

Internal causes of disease might include inherited or genetic defects, auto-immune disease (i.e. destruction of body tissues by the immune system), cancer (which may develop for many reasons), the ageing process and numerous others, many of which remain unknown to medical science.

Veterinary medicine is a composite of numerous different subjects and vets have to study topics as diverse as anatomy, physiology, biochemistry, nutrition, genetics, animal management, pathology, microbiology, parasitology and pharmacology as well as the more obvious clinical subjects of medicine, anaesthesia, radiology, animal breeding and surgery. Furthermore, the student has to consider these subjects as they apply to the whole range of relevant species. A degree in veterinary medicine is arguably the most wide-ranging of any.

It is clear that the sum of knowledge is now so great that no single veterinary graduate could possibly claim to have expertise across such a wide field. Most vets now confine their activities to just a small number of species within their own particular area of interest.

One important group of diseases are those transmissible from animals to humans. These are known as zoonoses and many are of major importance. The veterinary profession plays a vital role in controlling these diseases, so as to safeguard human health. A classic zoonosis, which is well known and feared, is rabies. This disease, which is spread by carnivores such as dogs and foxes, is invariably fatal to humans once clinical signs have developed. Strict quarantine legislation helped to protect the UK from rabies since the early part of the 20th Century. Political pressures lead to a relaxation of this policy in the 1990s, when dogs and cats were allowed to travel freely between EU countries (albeit provided they were micro-chipped and vaccinated against rabies) and extreme vigilance will be required to ensure that rabies does not again become established in the UK.

Possibly the greatest medical trauma to hit the human species in the recent past has been HIV/AIDS. This was first recognised in the early 1980s and has now spread worldwide, infecting and killing many millions of people and causing enormous economic damage, particularly in Africa. The origins of the HIV virus remained obscure for many years, but it is now generally accepted that it is a variant of a similar virus affecting chimpanzees. It is likely that humans first became infected by hunting and eating wild chimpanzees in West Africa. Clearly this could not have been predicted, as the chimpanzee virus was unknown at the time, but it does show the danger of infectious agents crossing from one species to another.

In the UK, bovine spongiform encephalopathy ("BSE" or "mad cow disease") is another disease where it is thought that the infectious agent jumped species, passing from sheep to cattle and then to humans. A vigorous and very expensive national campaign eventually eradicated it from cattle and fortunately the predicted epidemic in humans never materialised.

There are numerous other important zoonotic diseases worldwide, but attention has recently been drawn to mutants of the influenza virus originating from birds and pigs (avian and swine flu). There is every possibility, indeed some authorities say an inevitability, that mutation of these animal viruses will lead to major pandemics in the human population. Intensification of livestock production and the ease and speed with which humans (and animals) can travel freely around the world will be major factors in this unpalatable scenario. Extreme vigilance by the veterinary profession will be necessary to try and identify and eliminate these diseases before they become established and spread into the human population.

The remit of veterinary medicine is far reaching and vets play a major role in many important areas. This book is mainly concerned with the veterinary profession within the UK, but there is clearly a worldwide need for veterinary expertise and personnel.

Chapter Three
The history of veterinary medicine

MANKIND'S association with and use of animals extends back many thousands of years. Texts and art from ancient China and Egypt indicate that as far back as 2500BC attention was being given to animal husbandry and elementary forms of animal care. The Romans coined the term "veterinarius", meaning "one who was skilled in the care of animals" and a book was published in AD500 describing the work of the veterinarius.

There is little evidence of further progress until 1598 when an Italian, Carlo Ruini, published a book on the anatomy of the horse.

The fore-runners of modern veterinary surgeons in Europe were the farriers, who developed the skills needed to shoe horses. Until the early part of the 20th century horses were of course vital as a means of transport, providers of power in agriculture and for use by the military.

The job of the farrier was to improve the performance of horses by keeping their feet in good condition. This involved trimming the hooves and nailing on metal shoes to protect the feet and give better grip. The old saying "No foot, no horse" underlines the importance of the art of farriery.

Farriers began to take an interest in lameness and other ailments afflicting horses and in the absence of any other qualified persons they took on the role of "horse doctors". However their knowledge and skills were very rudimentary and often they would inflict more harm than good. In common with human medicine at that time, there was no understanding of the causes of most diseases and a total lack of effective treatments. What we would now see as useless and obviously harmful practices such as "blood-letting" were commonplace for both human and equine patients.

However a good understanding of equine anatomy developed early on. George Stubbs, the famous artist (who was not a veterinary surgeon), laboriously dissected horses in order to gain an intimate knowledge of their anatomy, which he then translated to his acclaimed paintings. His amazingly accurate and detailed book on the "Anatomy of the Horse" was published in 1766.

A desire to improve knowledge about the diseases of horses and farm animals and to properly train professionals led to the founding of the world's first veterinary school at Lyon in France in 1761. The Royal Veterinary College opened in London in 1791 and a rival college in Edinburgh in 1823. Interestingly, many of the early professors and teachers were human surgeons.

The horse was the animal of primary interest at that time, but the huge economic losses resulting from diseases in farm animals stimulated an interest in the study of their diseases also.

The Royal College of Veterinary Surgeons was established in 1844, giving the UK veterinary profession an official status. It should be pointed out that the Royal Veterinary College and the Royal College of Veterinary Surgeons are completely different entities despite the similarities in their names.

The Royal Army Veterinary Corps dates from 1796 and was established to try and improve the lot of army horses, many of which suffered wretched lives as a result of poor management and disease. It was thought that far more horses were lost as a result of ignorance and disease than on the field of battle. The term "veterinary surgeon" was coined to distinguish the army veterinary officer from the equivalent human medical officer and subsequently became used to describe any qualified veterinary professional. Even today this title is used to describe a graduate of veterinary medicine, even though he or she may never undertake any surgery. In other countries, such as the USA, the term "veterinarian" is more favoured.

From the latter part of the 19th century medical science advanced at a prodigious rate. Specific agents such as bacteria, parasites and later viruses were identified as the cause of disease and were related to known pathologies. "Aseptic surgery" was introduced (i.e. ensuring that both the surgeon and patient were suitably scrubbed with an antiseptic prior to the start of an operation) and this dramatically reduced the risk of surgery. Previously many patients had succumbed to infections introduced by the surgeon's filthy hands. Anaesthesia allowed pain-free and therefore more prolonged and complex operations to be performed, whilst radiology (X-rays) revolutionised many aspects of medical diagnosis. The pharmaceutical industry was born and new, exciting and effective drugs were developed to replace the largely useless, or even harmful, potions of former times.

Vaccination was discovered by Edward Jenner in 1796. He used cowpox material to immunise people against the deadly scourge of smallpox. Vaccines have since saved the lives of untold millions of humans and animals.

Some valuable anti-bacterial drugs were produced in the 1930s but the age of antibiotics only arrived with the development of penicillin in the 1940s. Penicillin was soon followed by many other life-saving antibiotics. Since then innumerable drugs have been developed to treat virtually every disease known to medicine, although the Holy Grail of an all encompassing cure for cancer is likely to remain elusive.

Nearly all these advances were made to service the needs of human medicine, which for obvious reasons has always held priority over veterinary medicine. However, anything that could be adapted for use in treating animals was quickly adopted by the veterinary profession. It has generally been the case that veterinary medicine lags a few years behind human medicine. The initial costs of novel medicines or medical technology often make them too expensive for use in animals at the outset, but inevitably most things become cheaper with time and they then frequently become economically viable for veterinary use.

The horse remained the primary target species for the veterinary profession until just after the First World War, when the rapid proliferation of motor vehicles and the mechanisation of agriculture meant that horses became largely redundant for working purposes. Horse numbers went into decline until the 1960s, when increasing affluence and leisure-time lead to a renewed demand for horses purely for recreation and sport.

As horses declined, vets turned their attention to farm animals, as there was a critical need for increased food production in the early 20th Century. Schemes were set up to rid the national herd of the scourges of the major infectious diseases such as swine fever, foot and mouth, tuberculosis and brucellosis and this was largely successful, although some of these diseases still recur regularly to this day.

Techniques in artificial breeding of farm animals, such as artificial insemination and embryo transfers developed, allowing farmers to improve the productive capacity of their livestock at a far greater rate than natural methods would allow. Vaccines, anti-parasitic medicines and antibiotics all played a significant part in the intensification of livestock farming and increased productivity.

Small animal medicine was largely ignored until the 1950s, but subsequently became the major growth area. Virtually all the advances made in human medical science have been applied to small animal medicine and surgery, such that nowadays dogs and cats in the UK can expect medical care little different from their owners.

The development of effective vaccines against the major infectious diseases of dogs and cats had a profound effect on the health and life expectancy of these animals and soon gained acceptance by pet owners. The steady source of income from these vaccines allowed vets to invest in better facilities and equipment and still remains one of the most important factors in small animal practice.

Chapter Four

The Royal College of Veterinary Surgeons (RCVS)

THE RCVS is the regulatory body for veterinary surgeons in the UK. It was established in 1844 by Royal Charter to be the governing body of the veterinary profession. Its duties are governed by the Veterinary Surgeons Act 1966. The RCVS safeguards the interests of the public and animals by ensuring that only those registered with the RCVS can carry out acts of veterinary surgery. On graduating with an approved degree in veterinary medicine the new vet is required to become a member of the RCVS and takes an oath that he or she will constantly strive to safeguard the welfare of animals under his, or, more often these days, her, care. The letters MRCVS indicate membership of the RCVS and this is the exclusive license to practice veterinary medicine in the UK.

The RCVS is made up of three distinct parts:

● **It is a statutory regulator** and as such has responsibilities set out in the Veterinary Surgeons Act 1966. It maintains a register of veterinary surgeons eligible to practise in the UK and also regulates veterinary education and professional conduct.

● **It is a "Royal College"**, exercising powers under its Royal Charter to award Fellowships, Diplomas and Certificates to veterinary surgeons, veterinary nurses and others, and to act as an informed and impartial source of opinion on veterinary matters to the Government and the wider public.

● **It also runs the RCVS Trust**, a separate charity established to promote and advance the study and practice of the art and science of veterinary surgery and medicine.

Disciplinary functions

A number of committees oversee the functions of the RCVS. These include the Preliminary Investigation and the Disciplinary Committees, which investigate and adjudicate on complaints against members raised by the general public. Complaints received from the public are first referred to the Preliminary Investigation Committee who will consider the complaint and seek further information about the problem from the member concerned. Most complaints are resolved at this point. A small number are referred further to the Disciplinary Committee, which can hold a public hearing, in effect equivalent to a court of law, against a veterinary surgeon whose alleged actions or behaviour may amount to serious misconduct, or who has been convicted of a criminal offence that may mean he is unfit to practice. If found guilty the member may be suspended or removed from membership of the College and thus lose his livelihood from veterinary practice. Generally no more than half a dozen such cases arise each year.

The College does not concern itself about the fees charged by members except where they are judged to be so extreme that they may constitute serious professional misconduct. Nor does the College adjudicate on cases of alleged negligence, which are dealt with by the civil courts.

Education and supervision

The remit of the Education Committee is to oversee and regulate veterinary undergraduate degree courses, continuing professional development (CPD) and the award of postgraduate qualifications. The College monitors the university veterinary schools in the UK (which are inspected by the RCVS on a regular basis) and also oversees the admission of oversees graduates to practice in the UK.

Graduates of the seven UK universities offering degrees in veterinary medicine automatically become MRCVS on graduation and payment of a fee to the RCVS. There are reciprocal arrangements whereby veterinary graduates of certain Commonwealth and some accredited USA veterinary schools can become MRCVS. Graduates of EU veterinary schools also have the right to register with the College and practice in the UK. Other foreign veterinary graduates can become MRCVS by passing entrance examinations set by the College.

The College is also concerned to ensure that veterinary surgeons in practice undertake adequate continual professional development (CPD). Practicing members are required to undertake and keep a record of an average of 105 hours of approved CPD over a 3-year period. New graduates are encouraged and expected to enrol in a formal programme to help them monitor their professional development in the first years after graduation.

The College is also responsible for awarding various post-graduate veterinary qualifications such as Fellowships, Certificates and Diplomas and maintains a list of those accredited with specialist status as a result of achieving appropriate higher qualifications.

Other committees include the Advisory, Public Affairs, Planning and Resources Committees, the RCVS Trust and the Veterinary Nursing Council.

The College issues a "Guide to Professional Conduct" annually to every member. This identifies the key responsibilities of veterinary surgeons to their patients, clients, the public and professional colleagues, as well as their responsibilities under the law. It is not a detailed rulebook, but it sets out fundamental principles that may be applied to all areas of veterinary practice. Veterinary surgeons are expected to comply with these guidelines and failure to do so would inevitably count against a member in the event of a disciplinary hearing. Veterinary surgeons in practice are required to carry professional indemnity insurance to cover them in the event of being sued for negligence.

The RCVS Practice Standards Scheme (PSS)

The PSS was launched on 1 January 2005. It is the only scheme representing the veterinary profession in general practice and was set up to:

● Establish a quality assurance framework to promote and maintain the highest standard of veterinary care

● To make more information available about veterinary practices and so give clients greater choice.

The PSS is currently voluntary and veterinary practices submit themselves to inspection at one of three levels depending on their facilities and the level of service they can offer to their clients. The three levels accredited are Core standards, General Practice and Veterinary Hospital. Inspections are rigorous and are carried out by a team of senior practitioners. Accredited practices are re-inspected every four years although spot-checks can be made at any time. Practices are encouraged to advertise that they are accredited under the PSS. Currently around 50% of all practices are registered with the PSS.

The RCVS maintains a register of members and veterinary nurses as well as a list of premises where medicines are kept, as required under the Veterinary Medicines Regulations.

Figures for 2009 show that there were some 23,000 members on the RCVS register, of whom 17,000 have a recognised UK qualification. 14,000 are in general practice, whilst the remainder work in universities, research, industry, for the Government or for charities etc. Practicing members are divided more or less equally 50:50 male to female, with female members predominating below the age of 40 and males above that age.

The RCVS is a completely separate body from the British Veterinary Association, which is the national representative body for vets in the UK and is concerned with supporting the role of vets and providing CPD and other services to its members.

Chapter Five

Training to be a vet

Applying to veterinary school

THE six established universities in the UK offering veterinary degrees are Glasgow, Edinburgh, Liverpool, Cambridge, London (Royal Veterinary College) and Bristol. A new veterinary school was set up by the University of Nottingham in 2006 and expects to produce its first graduates in 2011.

Compared to many other professions the number of places available to study veterinary medicine in the UK is rather small. Around 810 students entered the first year of the course and 115 entered the second year in 2008/9. The demand for places at veterinary school has increased greatly over the past 25 years or so. It may seem far-fetched, but the enormous popularity of the James Herriot books, TV series and films produced in the 1970s, which showed a somewhat romanticised version of veterinary life in the 1930s, sparked a huge amount of interest in the profession. This lead to a surge in applicants to the veterinary schools: something that has been maintained to the present day. On-going popular TV series such as Animal Hospital and Vets in Practice maintained the high and generally favourable profile of the profession with the wider public.

Stiff competition means that candidates must achieve very good A-level results if they are to have any hope of gaining a place at veterinary school. Grades AAB at A level would generally be the minimum expected. Suitable A-level subjects would normally be science-based and include biology, chemistry, physics or maths. However it may be possible to offer certain other subjects. 22% of entrants to veterinary school in 2008/9 already held a degree.

The veterinary course takes five years, except at Cambridge where it is six years. In addition to attending lectures, tutorials, demonstrations and practical classes, veterinary students have to work during many of the university vacations. In the early years they have to gain experience in aspects of animal care such as lambing, whilst later on they are required to undertake six months of extra-mural studies or "seeing practice", where they are attached to a veterinary practice, shadowing and learning from practitioners.

Veterinary schools normally interview candidates before offering a place and it is very important that in addition to excellent academic record candidates are able to show that they are very motivated to study veterinary medicine and have undertaken suitable work experience to support their application. Ideally candidates will have worked with a wide range of species including domestic pets, farm animals and horses as well as in a veterinary practice during their school holidays. Local kennels and catteries, farmers, riding schools, livery yards or zoos as well as veterinary practices should be approached for work experience by older children who are thinking of entering the veterinary profession. Clearly candidates who have owned and cared for their own animals, learnt to ride or engaged in other activities with animals will also be at an advantage at the interview.

Who is entering the profession?

As a result of the methods recent governments have chosen to fund university education, many undergraduates incur very substantial debts during the course of their higher education. Sadly, veterinary students fare worse than most, in that their course is longer and the pressures of their studies and requirements to "see practice" during the vacations means that they have limited opportunities to earn any money during their time at university. Some students rely on financial support from their families, whilst others graduate with debts, which may run into tens of thousands of pounds. This is a heavy burden for the new graduate entering veterinary practice, where the financial rewards in the early years are not great.

It appears that this deters students from poorer backgrounds from applying to read veterinary medicine. Surveys have shown that veterinary undergraduates come from higher socio-economic groups than most others. The typical veterinary graduate is a white female from a relatively affluent middle class background. Only a few come from ethnic minorities or very low-income families.

One of the major changes seen in the last 20 years or so has been the enormous increase in women entering the profession, which historically was the preserve of men. The first woman was admitted to the RCVS only in 1922. Even in the 1970s 80% of veterinary graduates were male. This has now totally reversed and current statistics show that some 80% are female. There are probably various reasons for this. Statistically girls achieve better A-level results than boys and nowadays universities are not allowed to discriminate as to whom they admit on the basis of gender, as certainly happened in the past.

The traditional image of a veterinary surgeon was perhaps of a somewhat "macho" individual who spent a lot of time wrestling with unruly cattle and horses and this may have deterred girls from entering the profession. The development of effective methods of chemically sedating large animals means that pure physical strength is no longer a pre-requisite for veterinary work. Furthermore the rapid evolution of small animal practice in the last 30 years or so may have acted as a further attraction for girls (whilst the increasing "fluffy bunny" image of small animal practice may be deterring some boys from becoming vets).

It is worth noting that women have now risen to the very top of the profession in many areas. There have been women presidents of the RCVS, the BVA and other veterinary organisations, a female Government Chief Veterinary Officer and many senior academics and professors, as well as successful practitioners.

Another change has been the increasing tendency for some veterinary schools to admit foreign students. These are required to pay hefty tuition fees and act as a good source of revenue to the schools. Figures for 2008-9 show that 12% of entrants came from foreign (non EU) countries.

The undergraduate veterinary course

The traditional undergraduate course is divided into pre-clinical, para-clinical and then clinical sections, spread over five or six years. There is a massive amount of information to be learnt and as the sum of knowledge increases so the pressures on the veterinary curriculum grows ever-more.

Pre-clinical subjects include anatomy, biochemistry and physiology: subjects which teach the nuts and bolts of how living creatures are put together and function. It is necessary to know how a normal healthy animal works before one can understand and treat the same animal when it is afflicted with a disease. One of the striking differences between the student of human medicine and the student of veterinary medicine is that the latter has to study a range of species, which may have many fundamental differences in terms of anatomy and physiology. For example, the digestive system of the dog is very different from that of the cow.

Para-clinical subjects include pathology, bacteriology, virology and parasitology -in other words looking at how diseases are caused, spread and inflict damage on the host species. Other topics include pharmacology (the study of medical drugs), animal husbandry, nutrition and genetics.

Clinical years are spent learning about medicine, anaesthesia, radiology, surgery and animal reproduction. During this time students will spend much time shadowing clinicians in the various clinical departments of the veterinary school, to which animals are referred by veterinary surgeons in general practice for specialist investigation and treatment.

The new veterinary course offered by Nottingham University is aiming to offer a more integrated form of teaching with the introduction of clinical material early on in the course.

Veterinary medicine is potentially concerned with the health of the entire range of living creatures, with the exception of humans. Clearly it would be impossible to cover such a wide diversity of species in an undergraduate course. Thus the veterinary student learns almost entirely about the common domestic species such as dogs, cats, horses, cattle, sheep, pigs and poultry and only touches on less commonly encountered species such as fish, reptiles, zoo or other exotic animals. In recent years it has become common for people to keep rabbits, guinea pigs and other small mammals as household pets and to expect these creatures to have access to quality veterinary care. The veterinary schools are somewhat belatedly beginning to recognise this and improve the quality of teaching in these areas, which formerly were largely ignored.

In some countries veterinary undergraduates are allowed to begin to specialise in certain species or groups of species, but in the UK there is still a desire to produce the "omni-competent" graduate. Clearly as the volume of knowledge expands this is not really possible and most veterinary surgeons now working in general practice confine their interests to either small animal, equine or farm animal work.

There is concern that the very high academic grades needed to gain a place on the veterinary course may not be needed for work in general practice, which does not really require an intellectual high-flyer. Indeed a lot of the work is mundane, routine and repetitive. Many well-respected senior members of the profession, who have had highly successful careers in practice, would be the first to admit that they would have had little chance of gaining a place at veterinary school today. There is a risk that very highly academic graduates may be rapidly disillusioned by the realities of life in practice after the initial burst of enthusiasm on graduating and there are fears that there will be a significant wastage as these people either move into other more academic areas or leave the profession altogether.

Chapter Six
Veterinary nursing

S MALL animal practice did not begin to evolve in any serious way until the late 1950s, when increasing affluence led to a demand for better health care for pets. At that time important advances were being made in medicine generally and the pharmaceutical industry was developing many novel and exciting drugs, such as new anaesthetic agents, analgesics (pain-killers), antibiotics, steroids and hormones to treat a wide range of diseases. Many of these could be used in dogs and cats and provided scope for small animal practitioners to offer far more than they could in the past.

Effective vaccines against the major infectious diseases of dogs and cats were developed and became accepted by the public, providing a good source of income to small animal practitioners. This allowed them to invest in more equipment and expand their services.

As small animal practice developed it became clear that the vets needed skilled personnel to assist them. Many practices employed some-one (usually a young woman, who was "good with animals") and trained them to undertake tasks such as holding animals for treatment, cleaning and preparing equipment, looking after in-patients, helping with opera-tions, monitoring anaesthesia and so on. This was not entirely satisfac-tory. It was evident that there was a need for properly trained individuals to assist vets in small animal practice and so the veterinary nursing profession came into being.

The original veterinary nurses were called Registered Animal Nursing Auxiliaries (RANAs) as the term "Nurse" was protected, referring only to those concerned with looking after human patients. The first RANA qualified in 1963 and the training was "in house", supplemented in some cases by attendance at a college. Over the years the training of veterinary nurses has evolved and become more tailored to the needs of modern practice.

To begin training as a veterinary nurse it is necessary to have a minimum of five GCSEs at Grade C or higher, or hold an Animal Nursing Assistant (ANA) or Veterinary Care Assistant (VCA) qualification.

The current route to qualifying as a veterinary nurse is via the RCVS Level 3 Diploma in Veterinary Nursing. Training takes two years fulltime, or three years part-time. Alternatively the student can undertake a Veterinary Nursing Foundation or BSc Honours degree in veterinary nursing at university. Full details on training options can be found on the RCVS or BVNA websites.

Qualifications are available either in small animal or equine nursing and there are now advanced qualifications at Diploma level for those wishing to progress further.

On qualifying, veterinary nurses are entered on the Register of Veterinary Nurses, which was established by the RCVS in 2007 to give veterinary nurses a more professional status and may use the letters RVN (Registered Veterinary Nurse). RVNs are governed by a professional code of conduct, similar to that of the MRCVS. They are also required to undertake continuing professional development, currently 15 hours per year.

In 2009 there were some 8,400 nurses listed or registered with the RCVS. The veterinary nursing profession is predominately female.

Today, qualified veterinary nurses have an extremely important role in most veterinary practices, many of which would find it impossible to function properly without them. RVNs are permitted to perform certain designated clinical procedures and minor operations. They are responsible for all aspects of the care of in-patients, administer medicines, hold animals for procedures, help with radiography, take and analyse blood and other laboratory samples, assist at surgery and undertake minor surgery themselves, monitor anaesthesia, run the pharmacy, liase with sales representatives from drug companies and much else. Nurses often hold clinics for various groups of patients such as geriatrics, or those needing to lose weight. Some nurses take a particular interest in nutrition and can give clients advice on this. Many hold "puppy parties", to educate owners on the care, feeding and health of their new acquisitions.

Veterinary nursing is not an entirely glamorous job. Sick animals vomit, defaecate and urinate – often to excess. A lot of the nurse's time is spent cleaning animals and kennels, laundering bedding and mopping floors. There is a constant need to maintain a high level of hygiene in the surgery. Operations are often bloody and messy and as much time can be spent cleaning up after an operation as in actually doing it. Instruments have to be washed and sterilised and surgical gowns and drapes laundered.

Most veterinary nurses work in general practice, but there are other career opportunities with pharmaceutical and animal feed companies, universities, research institutes, charities and so on.

Chapter Seven

Vets in practice

S OME people believe that in order to be a good vet one must "love animals". Whilst most vets would certainly like, respect and find animals and their diseases fascinating there is obviously a lot more to the job than just "loving animals".

Whilst it might be thought that a degree in veterinary medicine would naturally lead to a career in general practice, there are many other career options. Because the veterinary degree covers so many different subjects and areas of applied biology it offers scope in many different directions. Having said that, of the 16,641 home-practicing members on the RCVS register in 2009, 85% were classified as working in practice. Four percent worked in universities and colleges and a similar number for the Government in a variety of capacities. The remainder worked in research institutes, industry and commerce or for the army, charities, zoos etc.

Unemployment for veterinary graduates is, and always has been, minimal.

General practice

The majority of graduates start work in practice immediately after graduating. However some later transfer to other career paths if they find themselves unsuited to the life of a general practitioner (GP). General practice is broadly divided into small animal, equine or farm animal practice. In addition, there are specialist or referral practices to which general practitioners can refer more complex cases or unusual species.

Vets in practice are very much all-rounders, compared to doctors. The average GP vet will need to be the equivalent of a human medical GP, physician, surgeon, obstetrician, anaesthetist, radiologist and dentist, all in one. Obviously a GP vet cannot be expected to perform all these functions to the level of the equivalent human specialist, but most doctors would be amazed at the breadth of skills used by a practicing vet on a daily basis.

Examination of an animal

An animal presented to the vet may have any one or more of a vast number of potential problems. A human doctor would obviously question the patient closely to try and establish the nature of the problem. The first and foremost difficulty facing the vet is that the animal clearly cannot communicate directly and the owner is therefore the intermediary via whom the vet must try and establish some facts to aid the diagnosis. Therefore one of the requirements of being a good vet is having the ability to talk to owners and extract useful information from them in a short time.

Taking a thorough clinical history and then performing a full clinical examination are the bedrocks of making a diagnosis. A sound "bedside manner" is essential and many clients will judge the vet on his or her communication skills. The owner will be quizzed about the animal's age, behaviour, appetite and thirst, any problems such as vomiting, diarrhoea, coughing, breathing troubles, lameness, signs of pain, abnormal urination, vaccination status and so on.

The vet will then make a full clinical examination of the animal. This will follow more or less the same pattern, no matter which species is being looked at, although obviously modifications may be needed in some cases. The clinical examination will start with a look at the overall bodily condition of the animal. Is it unusually fat or thin? Has there been any change in weight recently? Does it look relaxed and comfortable, or anxious or in pain? Is the breathing normal as to rate, rhythm and depth? The age of the animal may suggest the likelihood of some problems more than others. The vet will then take the temperature via the rectum (an endless source of amusement to small children who might be watching). A raised temperature is often an indicator of infection. The pulse will be felt for rate, rhythm and strength. Next the colour of the mucous membranes of the eyes and lips will be examined and the skin tested for elasticity, which may indicate dehydration.

The vet will feel all over the animal's body for any lumps, bumps or painful areas and palpate all the external lymph glands and manipulate the limbs. The mouth will be opened and the teeth, gums, tongue and throat examined. Next the chest will be examined with a stethoscope. The heart rate and rhythm and the presence of any murmurs (abnormal sounds) will be noted. The lungs are checked as the patient breathes in and out, again listening for any abnormal sounds. The abdomen is then carefully and methodically checked by manual palpation, feeling for any unusual lumps, enlarged or shrunken organs, or evidence of pain. The eyes and ears may be examined with special instruments. The vet may wish to watch the animal moving to detect signs of lameness or possible neurological problems.

An experienced vet can perform a clinical examination quite quickly and gain a lot of useful information. Obviously the owner's history may well give a clue as to the area of the body affected, to which the vet will pay particular attention. However, very often the history is vague or non-specific. The owner's complaint is frequently something like "Oh he's just not right in himself" or "I know there's something wrong, but I don't know what".

Keeping careful clinical notes and records is essential for continuity, particularly as the animal may be seen by another vet at a later date. Virtually all practices these days keep computerised case records. Computerised systems also allow practices to send out reminders to clients when their animals need repeat vaccinations or other check-ups.

The clinical examination may be enough for the vet to make a reasonable diagnosis and suggest appropriate treatment. If this is not the case then further investigation will be necessary.

Blood tests are very commonly used to give information about a great number of different problems. The function of internal organs such as the liver, kidneys and pancreas can be assessed from a routine blood test. Blood counts assess the numbers of red blood cells, which are concerned with transporting oxygen around the body and the various white cells, which fight infections and provide immunity.

Numerous other chemicals can be detected in the blood and unusually high or low levels may indicate a specific disease. For example, in the common condition of diabetes the blood glucose level will be abnormally high. Frequently, rather than performing a single blood test the vet will ask for a number of tests to be done together in the hope that something will turn up to aid the diagnosis.

Other laboratory investigations might include looking at samples of urine, faeces or skin samples.

Most veterinary practices will be able to perform some laboratory tests "in house", whilst other samples may need to be sent to one of the many commercial laboratories available to the profession.

Sometimes biopsies (small samples of tissue) may be taken, either from external lesions, or from internal organs. Biopsy tissue is submitted to an expert histo-pathologist who will describe any abnormalities present. Biopsies are particularly used in the diagnosis of cancer.

More information about internal structures can be gained from X-rays and ultrasound scans, which are routinely performed by many vets. X–rays are best for looking at bones, whilst ultrasound is particularly good at looking at internal organs such as the heart, liver and kidneys and of course for diagnosing pregnancy. Heart diseases can also be investigated using an electrocardiogram (ECG).

More advanced high-tech scanning methods such as MRI (Magnetic Resonance Imaging) and CT (Computerised Tomography) are now widely available at private or university referral centres.

Sometimes a diagnosis can only be made by actually looking inside the body, either via an endoscope, or an exploratory operation. An endoscope is essentially a telescope, specially designed to look inside the body. Modern flexible fibre-optic endoscopes allow a skilled clinician to visualise the internal organs with great clarity.

All these investigations are used to try and establish what is wrong with the patient so that effective treatment can be given.

Surgery

Surgery is an integral part of most practices and techniques and equipment have improved greatly in recent years. Modern anaesthesia is considerably safer than in the past and allows vets to undertake prolonged and sophisticated operations and to safely anaesthetise young or old animals. Aseptic surgery is routine and so the risk of post-operative infection should be minimal, although veterinary premises have suffered, albeit to a much lesser degree, from the problems of MRSA, which has caused such havoc in human hospitals.

Immunisation

One of the major advances in animal and human health has been the evolution of vaccines against the major infectious diseases. It is easy to forget the devastation that serious infections caused before effective vaccines were available.

In the veterinary world many companion animals used to have a limited life expectancy due to the prevalence of diseases such as distemper, infectious hepatitis, parvo virus and leptospirosis in dogs and feline enteritis, cat flu and leukaemia in cats. Vaccination against these diseases is now routine and enormous numbers of lives have been saved. Even pet rabbits are now commonly vaccinated against myxomatosis and viral haemorrhagic disease.

Horses are routinely immunised against equine flu virus and tetanus, whilst there are a whole host of vaccines to protect farm animals against many infectious diseases.

Euthanasia

One of the realities of life, sadly, is that not all illnesses are treatable and owners may be faced with the unpalatable fact that their animal is not going to get better. One of the major differences between veterinary and human medicine is that vets have the legal choice of offering and performing euthanasia in appropriate cases, such as incurable illness or extreme old age. This is frequently a very difficult situation for both the owner and the vet. Owners obviously can be very distressed at having to make a decision of such magnitude and a good vet will be supportive and sympathetic, whilst trying to guide the owner to make the right choice.

Ultimately it is the welfare of the animal that is the priority and the vet will try and advise whether it is going to have an acceptable quality of life. Once the euthanasia decision is made, small animals will be given an intravenous injection of barbiturate, which instantly and painlessly leads to death. Horses may be similarly euthanased by chemical means, or may be humanely shot. Owners may or may not wish to be present and the vet will normally try and go along with their wishes. The whole process can be emotionally draining for the owner (and even experienced vets can find it a very difficult situation to deal with). However owners are often very grateful when an animal has a peaceful and dignified end to its life and ongoing suffering is alleviated. Not infrequently owners will say something along the lines of "I wish we had the same choice for ourselves".

Deceased pets may be taken home and buried in the garden, providing there is no risk of contaminating watercourses. However the practicalities of burying a large dog should not be under estimated. Nowadays most pets are collected from veterinary premises and cremated at a registered pet crematorium. Owners may have the choice of having their pet's ashes returned to them in a casket.

The different types of practice

Until the 1970s or 1980s many practices were truly "mixed" in that they treated domestic pets as well as horses and farm animals. Every town would have one or more, which would serve the needs of the different groups of animal owners in the locality. Larger cities would tend to have practices that focussed solely on small animals and there were a few rural ones that specialised in horses or farm animals.

Over the past 20 years or so there has been a marked decline in the number of farm animals in the UK, largely for economic and political reasons, whilst the number of leisure horses has increased significantly and small animal numbers have remained buoyant.

Knowledge and technology have progressed hugely in all areas of veterinary medicine and as a result it has become necessary for most GPs. to focus on one group of species. Although mixed practices still exist, the trend has been to concentrate on farm animals, horses or small animals. Even within mixed practices individual vets will often focus on one of these groups.

RCVS figures for 2009 show that around 53% of vets in practice were engaged in small animal work, 30% in mixed practice, 4% in equine and only 3% in large animal practice. The remainder did not specify their type of work.

The business aspects of practice

The vast majority of veterinary practices are privately owned businesses, traditionally belonging to a sole practitioner or a partnership of two or more veterinary surgeons.

Fees are set at the discretion of the partners and vary widely both across the country and even within the same area. There is obviously no equivalent of the NHS for animals and some owners are surprised at the high level of veterinary fees, having little idea about the cost of supplying medical services, or the true price of medicines. Pet and horse insurance is widely available to protect owners from unexpected veterinary fees and most vets strongly encourage owners to insure their animals.

The fact that owners are required to pay for veterinary care for their animals inevitably causes problems for those who are not insured or sufficiently well-off to meet unexpected costs. Vets are faced on a daily basis with animals needing treatment, but with the owner lacking the necessary financial resources to do so.

It has to be accepted that treating an animal is not the same as, for example, fixing a car and vets are conscious that they are dealing with living creatures, not machines. Vets will try to be as accommodating as possible and offer clients a level of treatment appropriate to their means, whilst at all times endeavouring to safeguard the welfare of the animal. However it is an unavoidable fact that veterinary practices are businesses and cannot survive without generating an appropriate income. Most subsidise their poorer clients, at the expense of the better-off. Sadly, in some case it may be that euthanasia is the only realistic option where the welfare of the animal cannot be guaranteed in the absence of any payment from the owner.

Fortunately there is a "safety net" provided by the major charities, such as the RSPCA, PDSA and Blue Cross, which provide veterinary services for the poorest members of society. However they may only help those on state-benefits and there is not a charity clinic in every part of the country.

Partnerships

Partners often employ young veterinary graduates to work for them on a salaried basis. These are rather confusingly called "Assistant Vets", although they are fully qualified. A typical partnership will also employ veterinary nurses as well as reception and administrative staff. Increasingly, larger practices hire a professional manager, who takes on the ever-growing burden of administering the business, allowing the partners to earn money by doing more veterinary work. The veterinary degree course offers no training in running a business and so vets really have to learn this "on the hoof". Some make better businessmen than others.

In the past it was the norm for a young vet to work in one or more practices after graduating, in order to gain experience and then either set up a new business or seek an opening in an existing partnership wishing to expand, or where a senior partner was retiring. The incoming partner would have to buy a share of the business, normally based on fixed assets such as property and equipment as well as goodwill. In recent years there has been some reluctance by young vets to join partnerships. This is in part for economic reasons. Young graduates carrying a substantial student debt may find it difficult to borrow funds to invest in a partnership, whilst the ever increasing value of property in the UK can make the value of old partnerships too expensive for youngsters to buy into. Additionally there is some evidence that the increasing proportion of female graduates may have a long -term effect on traditional partnerships. Women often take career breaks to raise children and some may not wish to make a heavy financial commitment. However there are many examples of female vets who have either set up their own business or successfully joined established partnerships.

Corporate practices

One interesting development in recent years has been the growth in corporate or joint-venture practices. Some of these have grown quite large and one now has in excess of one hundred affiliated branches and is a publicly quoted company. There are various business models, but they are generally financed by a business organisation, sometimes jointly with the veterinary surgeons or nurses working in the individual practices within the group. The practices share a common name and corporate branding but may cover a wide geographical area. They are administered centrally and can use their size to negotiate advantageous prices for medicines and other equipment.

There has been a degree of hostility between traditional partnerships and these newer businesses in some areas. The main benefit to young vets joining them is that the initial investment tends to be much lower than for a traditional partnership and a lot of the administrative burden is undertaken centrally. Corporate practice has focussed mainly on the small animal market.

Out of hours cover

All practices are required by the RCVS to ensure that owners have access to veterinary services 24 hours a day and 365 days of the year. Most provide their own out-of-hours cover and this has always been a considerable burden, as few are able to afford specific night-staff. Vets are often on duty all night and then have to continue to provide their normal daytime service.

There has been a trend in recent years towards the establishment of specific "out-of-hours" clinics, either run by a group of practices within a local area, or by commercial organisations on a nation-wide basis. This trend is likely to increase as younger vets demand a better work-life balance and legislation limits the number of hours employees can be asked to work per week.

Choice of practice

Owners have complete freedom of choice as to which practice they favour and are quite free to move from one to another, although this clearly may not be in the animal's best interests, as it is often better that the owner develops a good relationship with one practice. Some owners prefer the intimacy and personal service of a small single-handed practice, whilst others are looking for the best-equipped practice available, which larger businesses might be more able to provide.

The RCVS Practice Standards Scheme can give owners an indication as to the level of facilities offered by individual practices, but at the moment this is a voluntary scheme and not all practices belong to it.

Veterinary medicines

Veterinary practices stock most of the drugs and medicines they use on a day-to-day basis, which they source from wholesalers. Deliveries are generally daily, so there is speedy access to any unusual medicines, as needed. Clients also legally have to be offered the option of getting their medicines from other registered providers and there has been a growth in so-called "internet pharmacies", which often undercut vets.

All animal medicines are regulated by the Veterinary Medicine Agency (a Government body) and must be licensed for veterinary use. Each product has a designation which specifies who is allowed to prescribe it: veterinary surgeon, pharmacist or other suitably qualified person. The major important and potent drugs such as antibiotics, steroids, hormones, vaccines and strong painkillers are registered as Prescription Only Medicines –Veterinary (POM-V) and can only be prescribed by an MRCVS to animals under his or her direct care. This means that the vet must have examined the animal before prescribing the medicine and explains why a client cannot just ring up and demand antibiotics etc. for his pet without the vet seeing it.

Vets are also permitted to prescribe human medicines for use in their patients, but only if there is no licensed veterinary product for that condition or species. Many veterinary licensed drugs are the same as human medicines.

Chapter Eight

Types of practice

Small animal practice

THIS has been the major growth area in recent years and the creation of new practices has lead to intense competition in some places.

Small animal practices concentrate on dogs and cats. However, there is an increasing demand for better veterinary care for "small furries", i.e. rabbits, guineas pigs and hamsters, as well as birds, snakes, tortoises and so on. Many vets are happy to treat at least some of these minor species and information on their ailments is now increasingly available via up-to-date text-books and CPD. Others will refer less familiar species to a specialist.

Practices vary tremendously in what they offer and range from a single-handed vet, located in a high street shop, to impressively large and lavishly equipped multi-vet hospitals, offering the highest level of veterinary care. More complex cases may be sent to one of the many referral practices.

Virtually all practices will offer consultations by appointment and it is no exaggeration to say that the problems human patients often seem to encounter in getting a speedy appointment with their GP are rare in the veterinary world. Most practices will happily be able to offer same-day appointments and similarly there is seldom any significant delay in seeing a specialist.

Even the most basic small animal practice (classified as Tier 1/Core Standards under the RCVS Practice Standards Scheme) will offer consultations, preventative medicine (vaccinations, worming and parasite control), routine surgery under general anaesthesia and basic dentistry. These days most will be able to take X-rays and perform some laboratory work.

Dogs and cats can suffer from a very wide range of medical problems involving different organs or parts of the body. Many of these are similar to those suffered by humans, but others are species-specific. The cardio-respiratory, gastro-intestinal, uro-genital, nervous and endocrine systems are all commonly afflicted with a variety of ailments. Skin diseases are extremely common, particularly in dogs. Diagnoses are made by following the previously-described pathway of taking a clinical history, making a clinical examination and then performing ancillary diagnostic tests as needed.

Many of the medical problems encountered in certain pedigree dogs (and to a lesser extent in cats) are the result of years of selective breeding for extreme, or even bizarre, features considered desirable in the show-ring. Happily, as a result of adverse publicity, the relevant authorities are at last beginning to address these issues. *See Quicklook at Dogs.*

Basic routine operations in small animal practice include neutering male and female animals and removal of external lumps and bumps. Most vets are capable of performing more complicated operations such as stomach, bowel and bladder surgery and caesarean section. Specialist surgeons at referral centres are able to undertake advanced procedures such as brain, spinal or heart and lung surgery.

Dogs and cats are frequently the victim of road accidents and fractured limbs are commonly seen. Treatment of these obviously depends on the nature of the injury and may range from applying a simple cast, to relatively straightforward internal or external fixation with metal pins and plates, right though to major reconstruction by elaborate and complex methods. Many GP small animal vets undertake the more straight-forward orthopaedic procedures (the term "orthopaedic" refers to bone and joint problems), but may wish to refer more complex problems to a specialist.

The next level of small animal practices (classified as Tier 2 /General Practice under the RCVS PSS) would be better equipped and able to investigate and treat more complicated medical problems and perform more difficult operations and orthopaedic procedures. They might have diagnostic equipment such as ultrasound scanners, ECG machines and fibre-optic endoscopes. They would be able to undertake more advanced radiology and a wider range of in-house laboratory tests. Animals may be kept at the surgery so as to allow investigation and treatment of a wide range of medical and surgical problems.

Dentistry is an important part of small animal practice and some practices invest in advanced dental equipment.

Most practices at this level employ veterinary nurses.

Small animal veterinary hospitals

Small animal veterinary hospitals (a term reserved for those practices accredited at Tier 3 by the RCVS PSS) can offer a high level of care and diagnostic equipment, sometimes to the level of very high-tech and expensive machines such as MRI and CT scanners. They are able to keep in-patients in the hospital for prolonged periods for in-depth investigation and treatment of serious or complicated illnesses and are usually able to perform advanced surgical procedures. Veterinary hospitals are required to have residential nursing staff available for 24-hour care of in-patients and must comply with a very wide range of regulations and requirements as laid down by the RCVS. However their "bread and butter" is still the provision of consultations, vaccinations and routine surgery.

Equine practice

Equine practices serve the needs of horses and ponies and, to a lesser degree, donkeys.

There has been a significant increase in the number of horses in the UK in the past 30 years or so. The needs of professional horse-keepers, such as those involved in the racing industry and other major equine sports like polo, show jumping, dressage and eventing, as well as the leisure rider, has led to a demand for skilled equine practitioners and this has been a growth area for the veterinary profession.

There are many types of equine practice. These range from the single-handed practitioner who carries most of his equipment in the car and concentrates on making "home visits" to treat relatively straight-forward problems, through to the type of practice which makes home visits but also has a clinic to which horses may be admitted for more in-depth investigations and treatment. These may include facilities for operating under general anaesthesia. Finally there are large and lavishly-equipped hospitals and referral centres, where complex medical and surgical problems can be dealt with.

Diagnosing equine problems follows a similar pathway to that described above for small animals. The veterinary surgeon is dependent on the owner to provide the history and will then proceed to make a clinical examination. Obviously the size of the equine patient limits the amount of information that can be gained from, for example, external palpation of the abdomen. The equine practitioner will have to resort to the time-honoured long blue glove and arm up the rectum to examine the internal organs in more detail.

The size and strength of the equine patient, together with its often volatile and unpredictable temperament, means that care must always be taken to ensure the safety of both the vet and owner when handling horses. One of the most useful advances in equine medicine in recent years has been the development of effective sedatives for horses. These are given intravenously (i.e. directly into the blood stream) and greatly assist in safely examining and treating fractious individuals.

Blood tests and other aids to diagnosis such as radiology and ultrasound are as appropriate to horses as they are to small animals. Basic X-rays of the lower limbs may be taken at the horse's home with a small portable X-ray machine, but more complex radiology will need to be performed at the clinic. Very powerful X-ray machines are available to take pictures of the spine and pelvis, but this would usually have to be undertaken at a referral centre. Joint problems may be diagnosed and treated by arthroscopy, where a fine scope is inserted into the joint. Very long flexible fibre-optic endoscopes are used to examine the respiratory and digestives systems. Some centres are now able to perform MRI examinations of the lower limbs.

Most horses are required to perform some form of useful activity to justify their existence and this can range from the supreme athletes in the world of racing, show jumping, dressage, eventing and polo right down to the pony who is taken out for a gentle ride twice a week. The investigation, diagnosis and treatment of a wide range of lameness problems form much of the equine practitioner's workload. These problems can vary from very minor injuries or infections (particularly within the hoof) to all manner of other orthopaedic problems such as damaged tendons and ligaments, arthritis and fractures. The peculiar anatomy of the equine limb and the type of work horses perform are major factors in their susceptibility to lameness. Shoeing can be a factor in many lameness problems and vets often work with farriers to resolve such issues.

Lameness diagnosis can be very challenging. The process of "nerve blocking" is frequently used to try and pinpoint the site of the problem. This technique involves injecting small quantities of local anaesthetic at different sites, starting at the foot and working up the leg, to numb specific areas. Once the painful part has been rendered insensible the horse will appear sound again. Similarly local anaesthetic can be carefully injected into joints to try and identify areas of pain.

The old adage "They shoot horses, don't they?" is largely a thing of the past in that many fractures of the lower leg can nowadays be surgically repaired (unfortunately severe fractures higher up the legs are still largely impossible to treat). However, one has to remember that horses have an economic as well as sentimental value and whilst fractures and other injuries can be repaired successfully, it cannot always be guaranteed that the horse will return to its former athletic level. In these circumstances the owner may sometimes decide not to proceed with expensive treatment, but take the path of euthanasia.

Surgery for horses has improved dramatically in recent years, largely due to much better and safer anaesthesia. Historically the safe induction, maintenance and recovery from general anaesthesia in equines presented considerable problems. Their great weight and volatile temperament have always made general anaesthesia a risky procedure compared to smaller animals. Today anaesthesia can be carried out relatively safely in well-equipped hospitals staffed by skilled veterinary anaesthetists. Some minor surgery such as wound suturing and castration can be done under general anaesthesia in the home environment and even so-called "field anaesthesia" is much safer these days than in the past.

"Colic" is a blanket term used to describe abdominal pain in horses.

As a result of its enormous size and complexity the equine digestive tract is particularly susceptible to problems. These can vary from a build up of gas in the bowel, or a minor impaction, to life-threatening torsions or displacements of parts of the intestine. Most owners are able to recognise the signs of abdominal pain in a horse and will usually call the vet as an emergency. The vet must attempt to diagnose the precise cause of the colic by careful clinical examination and internal palpation. If a major problem is suspected the animal must be rapidly referred to a hospital, where if necessary, surgery can be performed. In the right circumstances a successful outcome can often be achieved – something that was quite rare in the past.

Horses can suffer from many other illnesses. Respiratory disease is particularly common and horses are prone to numerous problems caused by respiratory bacteria and viruses. Vaccination against the equine flu virus is commonplace and is compulsory for racehorses and those competing in other organised sports. Flu vaccine is usually combined with tetanus, as horses are particularly prone to this disease, which is generally fatal.

Some equine vets specialise in horse-breeding. Stud fees for top stallions and the value of premium foals can reach astronomical levels, particularly for race-horses. Owners are keen to ensure their mares become pregnant at the desired time and have a safe pregnancy and delivery. New technology such as ultrasound is used to assess the mare's reproductive tract and predict the optimum time for mating, as well as to make an early diagnosis of pregnancy and follow the development of the foal through to term. It is now possible to perform embryo transplants in mares, so that eggs from a valuable mare can be fertilised and implanted into a surrogate mother. Artificial insemination (AI) is also widely used and allows semen from a desirable stallion to be used more widely than could be achieved by natural methods. However AI is not permitted for racehorses, as the authorities fear it could be used unscrupulously, whilst owners of top stallions may want to limit the number of mares served by the stallion, to retain his exclusivity and enhance the value of the offspring.

One challenging task for the equine practitioner is making a pre-purchase examination of a horse for a prospective buyer. The term "to vet" derives from this examination. A standardised method has evolved whereby the horse is checked as thoroughly as possible to try and ensure it is free from defects and will be suitable for the use intended by the new owner. Unfortunately even the most skilled vet can only see what is evident on the day and cannot always predict future problems. Sadly, owners who buy a horse which then goes on to develop problems are sometimes keen to blame the vet and "vettings" are one of the more common causes of litigation against the veterinary profession.

Farm animal practice

Farm animal vets deal mainly with cattle, sheep, pigs and goats. Poultry medicine is more specialised, whilst fish-farming is probably the ultimate specialist area. There are periodic vogues for more exotic livestock such as alpacas, llamas, red deer and even ostriches and farm vets may have to quickly learn about these species if a client starts to keep them.

Farm animal practice has undergone major changes in the past 20 years or so. Largely for economic reasons many farmers in the UK have moved away from livestock keeping in favour of arable farming which is often more profitable. The poor profitability of livestock farming has been blamed on political manipulation of prices and the power of the major supermarkets to squeeze farmers' margins. For example dairy farming is one sector that has declined dramatically, as farmers have been claiming for years that their production costs exceed the price they are paid for their milk.

Livestock farming has declined more rapidly in some parts of the country than others and is now predominately found in south- and north-western England and parts of Scotland and Wales. This has created problems in regions of the country where few livestock remain, as the veterinary practices in those areas often turn their attention to more profitable small animal work and lose expertise in dealing with farm animals. There are serious concerns that welfare issues may arise in some areas of the country where there may be virtually no vets competent to deal with farm animals.

Even in those parts of the country where there are significant numbers of livestock the number of exclusively farm animal practices may have declined and the remaining ones will have to cover larger geographical areas, making travelling time a significant issue.

Farmers who remain in the livestock sector try to improve profitability by increasing the size of their herds or flocks and are always seeking to cut costs and improve yields either by changes in management systems or adopting new technology. Dairy farming is again a classic example. Years ago, many farms kept a handful of cows, which were milked twice a day by hand. Contrast that with the current situation where there are relatively few dairy farms, but the herd size may run into many hundreds and the whole milking process may be automated, using computer-controlled milking machines. Pig and poultry farming has undergone ever-increasing intensification and enormous numbers of animals or birds may be kept in individual units. Large units, where many animals are housed in a confined space, are always an ideal breeding ground for infections and welfare problems to develop.

Vets working in the agricultural sector have had to adapt to the needs of the modern agricultural industry. In days gone by, the farm vet typically provided a "fire brigade" service, turning out to treat individual animals with a problem. The classic James Heriot stories describe the vet stripped to the waist and struggling to deliver a calf in a dirty and draughty barn, whilst a grumpy old farmer chewing a straw made caustic comments about the vet's abilities. Although farm vets may still be called to treat individual animals and deliver calves, much of their work is concerned with safeguarding the health and welfare of the herd or flock by means of preventive medicine and increasing productivity by manipulating breeding.

Farm vets must therefore advise on a wide range of management and welfare issues. They must liase with the Government veterinary service that is responsible for controlling the more serious diseases of livestock on a national basis and also provides laboratory facilities for the investigation and diagnosis of diseases in farm animals. They may also need to talk to animal feed companies, breeding organisations and others.

The selective breeding of farm animals for better growth or production has of course been going on for many years, but some people are concerned that things may have gone too far. Dairy cows are now little more than milk-producing factories and are prone to serious problems such as mastitis (infection of the udder) caused by the unnatural size of and demands on their mammary glands. The massive amounts of milk they produce must obviously be fuelled by adequate nutrition and it is easy for welfare and disease problems to arise if the balance between feed input and milk production goes wrong. Beef animals have been bred to carry more and more muscle and in some cases their calves may be too big to be born by natural methods. In some breeds caesarean births are more or less the norm.

The expansion of knowledge means that few vets would be able to claim expertise in all areas of livestock farming and there is an increasing trend for specialisation, or at least having a particular interest in individual sectors such as dairy farming, beef, sheep, pig or poultry production.

Referral and specialist practice

Vets in practice can refer difficult cases, or those needing complex investigation or treatment to specialist referral practices. Traditionally these services were provided by the clinical staff at university veterinary schools. In recent years there has been an upsurge in privately -owned referral centres, serving both the small animal and equine sectors. The Animal Health Trust, based near Newmarket, is a charity involved in veterinary research, which also offers specialist treatments for small animals and horses.

Private centres are usually owned and staffed by vets who have achieved post-graduate qualifications to Diploma level and are recognised as specialists by the RCVS. Many are well known within the profession as they will almost all have worked in the universities at some stage, teaching students and be well recognised as authors of clinical papers and text-books and speakers on the conference circuit. One of the advantages of being in a relatively small profession is that specialists can establish their reputations quite quickly.

Specialist qualifications are available in most of the clinical disciplines. The more common areas of specialisation include internal medicine, soft tissue surgery, orthopaedic surgery (bones and joints) cardiology (heart), ophthalmology (eyes), neurology (nervous system), dermatology (skin), diagnostic imaging (X-rays, ultrasound and MRI), anaesthesia and oncology (the treatment of cancer).

Referral centres can offer very sophisticated levels of investigation and treatment of a wide range of medical and surgical problems. Major orthopaedic surgery, joint replacements, heart, lung, spinal and brain surgery, cancer treatment by means of surgery, radiation or chemotherapy, cataract removal and lens replacements are routine now: something which would have been unthinkable just a few years ago.

The provision of high-tech medical equipment and sophisticated treatments means that the fees charged by referral centres are often very considerable and in some cases approach those of human private medical facilities. Many clients would not be able to afford such fees without the benefit of pet insurance and indeed the viability of referral centres is rather dependent on the existence of a sufficient population of insured animals. Of course there are also wealthy owners and others, perhaps less well-off, but prepared to pay out of their own pockets to ensure the best treatment for their animals.

The danger is that as fees continue to escalate, so insurance premiums will rise and more owners will find that they can no longer afford to insure their animals. There is a view that the whole house of cards may collapse if insurers can no longer generate sufficient profits and decide to withdraw from the market.

Some veterinary surgeons (and others) are beginning to questions the moral issues involved in providing such highly sophisticated levels of medical care to pets, which clearly are totally out of reach for so many humans living in less-affluent parts of the world. At the time of writing a veterinary surgeon in my home-town in Hertfordshire can refer a dog for an MRI scan, with no waiting list and the choice of at least six such facilities within a 30-mile radius. There are many third world countries where there is probably not this number of MRI scanners available to serve the entire human population.

Questions arise as to how far we should go in prolonging the life of an animal – should we treat just because we can?

The counter-argument is that owners have freedom of choice and if they wish to lavish vast sums on the pets' health, then the veterinary profession should be there to provide the means to that end. For many owners their pet is a real part of the family and serious illness or the ultimate loss of the pet can be as devastating as the same thing happening to a human family member.

Chapter Nine

Other career options

Post Graduate training, research, academia and laboratory medicine

THE broad range of subjects studied in the undergraduate veterinary degree make it an ideal base from which to go on to a research or academic career, which might appeal to the more academically minded graduate, who may not be suited to a career in veterinary practice. Some students take a BSc degree during the veterinary undergraduate course, which can give a "taster" for research.

Post-graduate training tends to follow either an academic/research directed route, which would normal mean gaining an MSc or PhD, or for those looking for a career in a clinical discipline, signing up for a residency and then internship in the clinical department of a university or other institute. Clinical post-graduate qualifications are offered by the RCVS, firstly at Certificate and then Diploma level, which can lead to specialist-accreditation. Diplomas may also be gained in a variety of subjects via the European post-graduate veterinary boards.

The initial post-graduate research qualification that many prospective academics undertake is a Masters degree (MSc), which may be achieved in one or two years. An MSc may be purely research based, or may be part of a structured training programme in one area of interest, such as zoological medicine.

Research opportunities are available in all the subjects studied at undergraduate level, but funding is often a problem and the student will need to seek out a suitable body to finance an intended research project.

A PhD normally takes at least three years and requires in-depth original research in one specific area, either in one of the non-clinical sciences or in a clinical discipline. Successful completion of a PhD might then lead to a lectureship and progression up the academic ladder. University lecturers combine research with teaching students. Career progression is generally dependent on producing an on-going stream of quality research papers, published in the more prestigious scientific journals.

Some academics move away from the university environment and pursue their careers in other research institutes, the Government veterinary service, in a commercial veterinary laboratory or with one of the pharmaceutical companies.

Graduates intent on pursuing a clinical career normally try and find a place initially as "resident" in a clinical department. They will shadow and be tutored by senior clinicians. Residency will then lead to an internship, where they have more responsibility for clinical cases. RCVS Certificate examinations are offered covering a range of clinical subjects appropriate to small animal, equine, farm animal and zoo species.

Diplomas are offered in a similar range of subjects, but are at a much higher level and not normally undertaken until at least five years post graduation. Increasingly senior clinicians will seek diploma level qualifications from one of the European or American specialist veterinary boards. Many clinicians seeking to advance their skills work abroad, particularly in the USA, which has a history of funding universities and research rather better than our own.

Graduates who have achieved Diploma or Board-certified status may apply to the RCVS for accreditation as a recognised specialist in that subject. Such specialists tend to continue working in university clinical departments, undertaking clinical duties, research and teaching students and hope to rise up the academic career ladder, or transfer to a referral centre in the private sector. Financial rewards are normally considerably better in the private sector.

The Government veterinary service

The Government employs some 850 vets in who work in a variety of different areas.

The Department for Environment, Food and Rural Affairs (DEFRA) employs vets whose role is to monitor animal health at a national or international level and prevent the spread of those diseases of major economic importance, or where human health might be jeopardised. Their remit is to protect the animal population (and in some cases the human population) from major epidemic diseases such as BSE, foot and mouth, avian "flu and tuberculosis and to take action as necessary when these diseases do occur.

A number of important diseases are classified as being "notifiable" and vets in practice are required to report any suspicions about these to the Government veterinary service, who will then investigate and take appropriate action.

In recent years the Government veterinary service has had to deal with a series of catastrophic and hugely expensive outbreaks of diseases affecting livestock. These diseases, which are of enormous economic significance, are generally controlled by identifying and destroying infected animals and imposing strict quarantine or movement-restrictions on infected premises. Public disquiet at the sight of piles of burning carcases is understandable and it is often asked why these diseases cannot be controlled more humanely or by use of vaccines. The short answer is that it is all down to economics and Government policy.

For example, for foot and mouth disease, there are vaccines available, which are used in other parts of the world, but the long-term cost of having to vaccinate every cow, sheep, pig and goat in the country would be massive. Vaccines are seldom 100% effective and it is likely that cases would still occur at a low level. Furthermore, the export of livestock and meat products to other countries could be jeopardised if the disease was seen to be endemic, or vaccination was routinely carried out, in the UK. Some countries require animals for export to be blood-tested to show they are free from diseases like foot and mouth and it may be impossible to differentiate vaccinated from infected animals. This is because the antibodies in the blood resulting from vaccination may be indistinguishable from those derived from an infection.

Government regulation of the import and export of animals is designed to prevent the spread of disease across the world and the risk of new diseases reaching our shores as a result of global warming, or other factors, has to be constantly monitored.

There are real concerns that if global warming happens new diseases will start to arrive in the UK, particularly those spread by insects or other blood sucking parasites like ticks. The recent arrival of blue tongue disease from Europe is a classic example of how this can happen. The virus is transmitted to sheep and cattle by biting midges, which were blown across the Channel from Holland. The milder climate of recent years allowed midges to survive in areas where they would not previously have been able to do so.

Rabies is a disease, which has obvious implications to human health, and there has been a long history of quarantine of imported dogs and cats to prevent its establishment in this country. In recent years the Pet Travel Scheme has been introduced to allow suitably vaccinated and micro-chipped animals to enter our shores from the EU and some other countries. This scheme has to be carefully monitored by the Government veterinary service.

Allowing freedom of travel of animals obviously encourages the spread of diseases and since the Pet Travel Scheme was initiated there have been a substantial number of cases of dogs contracting "exotic" infections in, for example, southern Europe and bringing them back to the UK. This presents problems, as UK vets may not be familiar with these diseases.

A number of other Government agencies such as Food Standards Agency, the Meat Hygiene Service and the Veterinary Medicines Directorate exist to regulate, monitor and maintain standards in different areas of animal health or production. The Veterinary Laboratory Agency provides a laboratory service for the investigation and diagnosis of disease in livestock.

Commerce and industry

A number of veterinary graduates find employment in commerce and industry. The major pharmaceutical companies producing veterinary medicines employ vets either within their research departments, or in areas such as product-support or sales and marketing. They often employ vets who have had some experience in general practice to act as veterinary advisers, answering queries about their products from practitioners and disseminating information about new drugs.

A small number of vets work in the meat industry inspecting livestock prior to slaughter and then checking the carcases to ensure that the meat is fit for human consumption.

Relatively small numbers of vets find employment in a variety of other areas.

The Army

The Royal Army Veterinary Corps (RAVC) was established in 1796 to look after the needs of cavalry horses, which were then obviously of vital national importance, but suffered horrific losses, not only at the hands of enemy forces, but also as a result of poor management and disease. Today the RAVC still deals with the few remaining horses in the army, used for ceremonial purposes, but has a more important role in looking after the health of dogs used by the military for detecting explosives, protecting military bases etc.

Charities

The major animal charities such as the RSPCA, Blue Cross and PDSA employ vets to run clinics providing veterinary care for people on low income (usually those receiving state-benefits) who cannot afford private veterinary fees. There are many other animal charities that operate both in the UK and abroad to safeguard animal health and welfare, either targeting one specific species or many. Some charities rely on volunteer vets to undertake short-term projects abroad.

Zoo, conservation and wildlife medicine

This has been a growth area in recent years and vets can now gain post-graduate qualifications in these disciplines. Larger zoos may employ one or more vets to look after the health of their animals whilst there are a few specialist veterinary practices that provide veterinary care for zoo animals, either nationally or internationally.

Dealing with wild animals, either kept in captivity, or in their natural environment, presents some special problems. A large zoo may have many hundreds of different species, including insects, fish, snakes, amphibians, birds and mammals ranging in size from a mouse to an elephant.

For many of these species there may be only limited data on their basic biology and physiology and there are very unlikely to be any medicines specifically licensed for use in them (virtually all veterinary medicines are only licensed for use in the common domestic animals). One cannot just presume that because a medicine is safe in one species that it can also be used in another. For example aspirin and paracetamol are highly toxic to cats, as is penicillin to guinea pigs. Over the years zoo vets will have learnt which medicines can safely be used in various species and it is important that this knowledge is shared, so that others may benefit.

The handling of wild animals can also be problematic. Even zoo animals bred in captivity may never become truly used to being with humans and some are potentially very dangerous. Such creatures often have to be sedated or anaesthetised before they can be safely handled for clinical examination or treatment. In the wild, animals may have to be moved from one area to another, for example to avoid losses from poaching. Frequently the only way to do this is by chemically immobilising them, before they can be put on to a lorry and moved to their new home.

The darting of wild animals started in the early 1960s, when the Kariba Dam was being built, in what was then Rhodesia. An enormous area, teeming with wildlife, was going to be inundated as a result of the new dam across the River Zambezi and it was decided to capture and relocate as many wild animals as possible (a project given the name Operation Noah). A very powerful new drug (M99) had recently been developed and this was found to be very suitable for immobilising wild animals when injected into them by means of a dart fired from a specially adapted rifle. The same drug remains a useful product for darting wild animals to the present day, although a number of newer anaesthetic and sedative agents are also in common use.

This drug was also quite a popular for field anaesthesia of horses in the UK in the 1970s, but rather fell out of favour when it became evident that it was extremely toxic to humans. Accidental self-injection, or even a spillage on the skin with a tiny amount of the drug, could be fatal.

Darting of wild animals is a skilled job, requiring a lot of experience in order to minimise risk to the patient. Either a modified rifle is used to fire the dart, or in a more confined space, a blow-pipe can be effective.

Darting large animals such as elephants and rhinos in the wild may have to be performed from a helicopter, an even more challenging job!

Another problem and responsibility facing the zoo vet is that some species are highly endangered and as a result may be extremely valuable, not just in biological terms, but also financially. The A-list Celebrity zoo animal is undoubtedly the giant panda from China. This animal is so much in demand that the Chinese authorities charge foreign zoos huge amounts of money to borrow and exhibit pandas. $1 million per year is said to be paid by some US zoos for this privilege. Clearly the health of these animals is paramount and if such a valuable creature falls ill the zoo is going to want the very best veterinary specialists in the world to be called in without delay.

Some zoo vets specialise in reproduction, which is clearly important in the case of endangered species, some of which may not breed easily in captivity. The giant panda is the obvious example of this, being notoriously coy about mating in a zoo environment. Artificial insemination is now used quite widely to improve on nature. Pregnancies can be diagnosed and monitored using ultrasound and intensive-care facilities can be provided to care for the new-born if needed.

Chapter Ten

A typical mixed practice

MIXED practices still exist and are often relatively large in size, with individual vets within the practice able to concentrate on small animals, horses or farm animals.

The following is a description of a hypothetical mixed practice based in a market town in the West Country.

Six partners ranging from 65 to 30 years of age own the New Millennium Veterinary Practice. Alison and Ruth look after the small animal clients; David and Sarah are responsible for the equine side of the business, whilst Mike and Steve deal with farm animals.

The practice also employs six younger assistant vets on a salaried basis. Three of them work on the small animal side, whilst the other three divide their time between horses and farm animals.

All practices are obliged to ensure that their clients have access to emergency veterinary care 24 hours a day, 365 days a year and so the New Millennium vets have to work on a rota to cover the nights and week ends. One of the problems of running a mixed practice is that vets who work exclusively in, for example the small animal department, may feel they lack the skills to provide emergency cover for the equine and farm clients. At New Millennium the small animal vets just cover small animal emergencies whilst the other vets cover horses and farm animals between them. Night calls vary in their frequency, but a night seldom goes by without a call-out of some kind and often there may be several. The duty vet will normally have a half-day off after a night on duty, but even so it can be difficult to cope with a busy morning's work if the previous night's sleep has been seriously disrupted.

The practice is located in purpose-built premise on the edge of the town, which the partners were lucky enough to purchase ten years ago.

Formerly it operated from a large house nearer the town centre, which was originally the home of the vet who founded the practice in the 1930s. The practice outgrew these premises in the 1990s and desperately needed to relocate to somewhere with more space and parking.

The current premises provide good facilities for treating small animal patients and have recently gained Tier 2 (General Practice) accreditation under the RCVS Practice Standards Scheme. There is a waiting room and reception area, three consulting rooms, a kennel area where in–patients can be kept, a treatment room, a pharmacy, a sterile operating theatre, X-ray and ultrasound rooms, a laboratory and a comfortable rest-room for the staff. The practice is therefore able to undertake a good range of investigations, treatments and operations and there is a good specialist small animal referral centre within 20 miles where more complex cases can be sent.

The New Millennium is fortunate to also have space for a couple of stables and a small barn where horses can be X-rayed and undergo investigations such as ultrasound and endoscopy. There is also a "knock-down" stable where horses can be anaesthetised for minor operations. The Equine Hospital at the University of Bristol Veterinary School is within relatively easy reach for the referral of horses needing specialist treatment.

Occasionally the stables are also used to accommodate farm animals needing treatment or surgery, which cannot be done at the farm.

Importantly there is a large car park, something that was lacking at the former premises and is essential to allow clients to unload animals near to the front door.

Two qualified veterinary nurses and two trainees are employed to mainly look after the small animal patients, but also to help when horses come into the clinic. Several part-time receptionists and office staff complete the team. The practice has recently taken on a manager, who will free the partners from a lot of administrative duties.

The small animal practice has grown rapidly in recent years as the population of the town has increased, with the establishment of some new industries nearby and a large new housing estate.

The equine side has also increased, as there is a growing population of horses in the area. There are two riding schools and several livery yards close by. The majority of the horse owners are private individuals with leisure horses, but the practice also looks after two studs and has a number of clients involved in show jumping, eventing and point-to-point racing.

The farm side of the practice has declined to some extent as several local farmers have given up keeping livestock in recent years. However a couple of the dairy farmers decided to buck the trend and expand their herds and now run very large units which require a lot of veterinary input. There are still a good number of beef and sheep enterprises in the area and a couple of wealthy "hobby farmers" have recently established herds of alpacas which has provided a new and interesting challenge for the farm vets.

A working day

The surgery opens its doors at 8.00 a.m. and the staff switch the phones over from the night service. Calls start coming in from horse owners and farmers needing visits and small animal clients begin to drop in animals that have been booked in for investigations or operations. There is a daily delivery of drugs from a wholesaler and this usually arrives early on.

Small animals

Alison and one of the small animal assistants start consulting at 9 o'clock. Consultations are booked at 10-minute intervals and go on until 11.00. Ruth stays behind the scenes to start the day's operations and deal with the in-patients.

Alison's first consultation is nice and easy. A farmer client has just bought a new Border Collie to train as a sheep dog. He is nine weeks old and due to have his first vaccinations. Alison checks him over carefully and pronounces him to be a good healthy specimen. She administers the vaccine and dispenses some worming medication and flea drops. The pup will need to come back in 2 weeks for a second vaccine and Alison reminds the farmer to get him micro-chipped at the same time.

Next comes Tigger, a cat with a hugely swollen face. He is a notorious fighter and Alison quickly diagnoses an abscess, almost certainly the result of a fight with another cat. The abscess will need to be drained and cleaned under a light anaesthetic and so the owner leaves him for this to be done.

The next patient is also a cat, which the owner found that morning in a rather sorry state, with blood on his face and dragging a back leg. Alison makes a careful clinical examination, noting an abrasion on the face and scuffed claws on both front feet. The cat's breathing is a little laboured and one hind leg feels very unstable. All the evidence points to a road accident. Alison advises the owner that the cat will need to be admitted for X-rays and treatment for pain and shock. Fortunately the cat is insured and so the owner is happy for him to have any necessary treatment. Alison hands the cat over to Ruth who is puts him on an intra-venous drip and administers pain relief and antibiotics. He will be X-rayed later in the day.

A couple of routine dog and cat booster vaccines follow and then another puppy arrives for its second vaccinations and micro-chipping. Micro-chipping involves injecting a tiny implant, the size of a grain of rice, under the skin between the shoulder blades. The micro-chip contains an electronic code, which uniquely identifies the animal for the rest of its life. The micro-chip details are registered with a central office and rescue centres and vets will routinely scan stray animals and if a chip is found the animal can hopefully soon be re-united with its owner.

Next a little girl and her mother come in with their two pet rabbits for myxomatosis vaccine. Myxomatosis is very common in wild rabbits and can spread to pet rabbits via fleabites. It is usually fatal and so the practice encourages owners to vaccinate their rabbits. The mother comments that one of the rabbits seems wet under its jaw and is not eating well. Alison looks inside the mouth with a scope and notes that several of the molar teeth have sharp spikes, which are digging into the cheek. This is a common problem in pet rabbits and often indicates a lack of fibre in the diet. Alison explains that the rabbit needs to be admitted so that the sharp spikes can be removed under general anaesthesia. The mother agrees to book the rabbit in for this to be done tomorrow.

The next dog is a regular visitor. Sam is an aged and somewhat overweight Labrador who suffers from arthritis of his hips. He has been on anti-inflammatory tablets for some time and has to have a check-up so that more tablets can be prescribed. His owner is happy with his progress and Alison is pleased to note that his weight has dropped by three kilos since she last saw him and advised that he should go onto a low-calorie diet to make him lose weight. Obesity in pet animals is becoming as big a problem as it is in their owners.

The last morning appointment is a difficult one, which Alison has been anticipating, but not looking forward to. The owner is an elderly lady and Susie, her much-loved terrier, has been on medication for heart disease for several months. Sadly her condition has deteriorated recently. She is 16 years old and is now nearly blind and despite the medication is coughing all the time and has a swollen belly due to fluid retention. She is also starting to become incontinent. Her owner is very upset, but knows that the end is nigh and feels that Susie should be put to sleep to prevent any further suffering, as her quality of life is now so poor. After a long discussion with Alison they agree that the time has indeed come.

Alison has to get the owner to sign a consent form to say that Susie should be put to sleep and then talks her through the procedure. The old lady wants to stay with Susie, so Alison gets one of the nurses to come in and hold the dog, whilst she slips a needle into the vein and injects a strong barbiturate solution. Susie goes into a deep and peaceful sleep from which she will not awaken. The owner asks that the body should be cremated and the ashes returned to her. Despite her years of experience Alison finds these consultations very difficult and stressful. She spends some time comforting the old lady and will later write her a note of sympathy.

It is now time for a welcome coffee and a chance to make a couple of telephone calls to owners who have rung in with queries about their pets' treatments or seeking advice.

Normally after morning consultations Alison would help Ruth who has been working her way through the day's operating list. However just as she sits down for her coffee a call comes in from a client whose elderly Great Dane has "collapsed". Normally clients are encouraged to bring their animals to the surgery whenever possible, but when they cannot the vets will make house-calls.

The practice owns a van, which is kitted out as a veterinary ambulance and Alison and one of the nurses set out to visit the collapsed dog. As is often the case they find there is no real drama. The dog is elderly, suffers from arthritis and finds it difficult to get up from a slippery kitchen floor. Alison checks the dog over thoroughly and then prescribes some anti-inflammatory medication and advises the owner to keep it off slippery floors!

Meanwhile Ruth has been operating since 9 o'clock. Every day around five or six routine operations are booked in. This allows for some flexibility, as inevitably other cases will arrive during the day, which will also need surgery. Today's list is pretty typical: two female cats to spay, a dog to castrate, a dog to have his teeth scaled and polished under general anaesthetic and a female dog with a mammary growth to remove. All the animals coming in for surgery are checked over by the vet and older ones usually have a blood test to check they are not anaemic or suffering from liver or kidney problems prior to being anaesthetised. Normally a sedative/painkiller "pre-med" is injected an hour or so before the animal is anaesthetised.

Most animals are given an intra-venous injection to induce anaesthesia and then are maintained on gas via a breathing tube inserted into the windpipe. The veterinary nurses prepare the patient for surgery by clipping the hair and thoroughly cleaning the operation site with antiseptic. The surgeon scrubs her hands thoroughly, puts on a sterile gown and gloves and then opens a pack of sterile instruments.

A nurse will monitor the anaesthetic carefully during the operation, regularly taking and recording the patient's pulse and respiratory rates. Once the procedure is completed the animal is allowed to wake up. The practice prides itself on ensuring that animals that have undergone surgery are given adequate pain-relief and usually additional painkillers will be injected and often the animal is sent home with analgesic tablets for a few days. Most animals undergoing routine operations are sent home later in the afternoon. It is an interesting fact that dogs and cats seem to tolerate surgery far better than humans and owners are often amazed to see their pet skipping out of the surgery quite happily after an operation.

After a short lunch break Ruth takes over the afternoon consultations whilst Alison attends to the animals that she admitted earlier. The cat with the abscess is anaesthetised and the abscess opened to release a flow of foul-smelling pus. Cats are notorious fighters and the small puncture wounds they inflict usually turn into putrid abscesses, as cat teeth can harbour some particularly unpleasant bacteria. The cat will go home with a course of antibiotic tablets.

The cat involved in the road accident case is X-rayed. There are some shadows on the lungs, which suggest there may have been some internal bleeding and there is a clean fracture across the middle of the left femur. Alison decides to continue with the treatment for shock and pain and then operate on the cat tomorrow when it is more stable. The fracture should be relatively easy to fix by inserting a steel pin down the bone. Cats usually do very well after this kind of injury.

Evening surgery starts at 5 o'clock and runs until 6.30. Alison is on duty that night and has to field all the small animal emergency calls. It is impossible to predict what each night will bring. Sometimes they are quiet but on other occasions she may be called out several times.

Horses

David, one of the equine partners, has also had a busy day. He spends most of his time "on the road" visiting horses at their homes. He has to carry all the equipment he will need in the back of his car and this includes a wide range of medicines, vaccines (in a small battery operated cool box) bandages and dressings, a stethoscope, a thermometer, kit to remove horseshoes and pare out the feet and dental equipment to allow examination of the mouth and rasping of the teeth. He also carries a portable X-ray unit, which fits into a box no bigger than a small suitcase, an equally small ultrasound scanner and a fibre-optic endoscope suitable for inspecting the upper respiratory system.

The morning calls today include a visit to a livery yard where half a dozen horses need their annual flu and tetanus vaccines and a couple also need a dental check-up. This involves inserting a large metal mouth gag to open the jaws and then, after careful inspection and palpation of the teeth, any sharp edges are taken off with specially designed rasps. These types of dental problems are very common in horses, as unlike humans, their teeth continue growing throughout life. Sharp spikes on the teeth can make eating uncomfortable and also cause pain when the horse is being ridden.

The next call is to see a lame pony. The feet are unshod, overgrown and split and the affected hoof is warm to the touch. David suspects an abscess in the foot and after carefully paring the sole of the foot with a sharp hoof-knife is pleased when a jet of pus shoots out, confirming his suspicions. He applies a wet poultice and bandage to the foot and tries to politely advise the owner to get the farrier in more frequently, so as to prevent this type of problem in the future.

An emergency call then comes in from a worried owner who has found her horse rolling around on the floor and obviously in distress. This sounds like a case of colic and so David sets off to see it straight away. He asks his office to see if one of the other vets may be able to pick up the other calls he has scheduled that morning.

On arrival it is obvious that the horse is in serious trouble. It is clearly in severe pain, is sweating profusely and has a very rapid heart rate. The colour of the eye membranes is much darker than normal. David sedates the horse and injects a strong painkiller intravenously. He dons a long glove and inserts his arm carefully into the horse's rectum. It is apparent that there is something gravely wrong, as he can feel distended loops of bowel further forward in the abdomen. It is likely that the horse has torsion of part of the intestine and emergency referral to the university hospital for surgery offers the only hope of a successful outcome. Luckily the horse is insured and the owner has suitable transport. David quickly "phones the hospital and the horse is soon on its way. He hears later in the day that surgery was performed and a length of twisted bowel removed. Fortunately, because the case was diagnosed and referred so quickly the horse makes a full recovery, although it will be off work for many months to come.

After a quick lunch break David sets off to look at a horse 25 miles away, which one of his clients is hoping to buy. He wants David to undertake a pre-purchase examination or "vetting" in order to tell him whether the horse is healthy and likely to make a good hunter. There is a standardised five-stage procedure for performing a vetting. This is designed to put the animal through a very thorough examination and involves looking at it at rest, being trotted up in-hand, exercised, rested and then trotted up again. The eyes, teeth, heart, lungs, skin, spine and limbs are all carefully examined and a blood test is taken to ensure that it has not been given any medication which might disguise lameness or alter its behaviour. David is happy that this horse has no problems and is suitable for the purpose intended. He phones the prospective purchaser to give him the good news and will later send a full written report.

David then returns to the surgery to catch up on some paper work and "phone calls. He is on call for the equine and farm side of the practice that night.

Farm animals

The farm animal vets also spend their days "on the road" and they too need to carry all their equipment in the car.

Mike has scheduled most of his morning to be with the practice's biggest dairy farmer. At this time of the year he makes a weekly routine visit, mainly to check cows for pregnancy and to look at any which are having problems getting in calf. Milk production depends upon cows producing calves regularly to maximise their yield. Gestation in a cow lasts for nine months and ideally the farmer wants the cow to be pregnant again within three months of having her calf. This is not always easy to achieve, particularly in high-yielding milkers, where the demands of a heavy lactation can reduce fertility levels. Much of Mike's time is spent trying to maintain the fertility levels of the herd and this may involve taking and analysing blood samples to ensure there are no abnormalities or deficiencies, as well as physically examining the cows. He may also have to liase with feed manufacturers to ensure that the cows' nutrition is spot-on.

Today there are 28 cows for pregnancy testing. This is done by the time-honoured "arm up the backside" technique, but nowadays an ultrasound scanner is used to look at the ovaries and uterus, which is rather more accurate than the old-fashioned manual palpation method. Cows that are not pregnant have to be examined carefully, to try and find out why they have not taken, and various hormone treatments may be used to try and bring them into oestrus so that they can be inseminated. A number of cows that have recently calved are also checked to make sure their reproductive tracts are healthy and free from infection.

The cowman next asks Mike to have a look at several lame cows. This is not an easy task, as cows are not trained to lift up their feet for inspection in the same way as horses. Each cow has to be cajoled into a crush (a steel cage, designed to hold it securely for examination). The lame leg is hoisted with a rope and strapped to a metal bar so that the vet can inspect it without too much risk of being kicked. Examination shows that all the cows have soft feet and infection between the toes. Mike asks whether the cows are spending more time standing in wet or muddy conditions and advises the use of a medicated footbath to harden the feet and kill the infection.

Mike then spends some time with the farm manager discussing a problem with mastitis in the herd that has been causing concern. Mastitis is a big problem in high-yielding cows and can be associated with problems with the milking machine, amongst other things. Mike advises that technical checks are made on the machine and arranges for milk samples to be submitted to the laboratory to see what type of infection is present.

After lunch Mike visits one of his beef farmers who has a problem with respiratory disease in his calves. Mike knows the farm well and suspects the problem will be largely due to overcrowding in a poorly-ventilated building. He has tried on previous occasions to get the farmer to use a different building for his calves, but the farmer's memory is short and every year he repeats the same mistake. Mike takes some blood samples and swabs from the calves to see if any particular organism can be identified and puts them on a course of antibiotics and anti-inflammatory drugs. He tells the farmer to open up as many doors and windows as possible to improve the ventilation.

He then calls in at another beef farm to check on a cow, which had a caesarean operation yesterday. She seems to be doing well and the farmer is relatively happy as she had a good calf, which will at least help to offset the cost of the operation.

The last call of the afternoon is to look at some sheep that are suffering from sore and weepy eyes. Mike diagnoses conjunctivitis and arranges for the owner to pick up tubes of antibiotic eye cream from the surgery. He then head back to base to catch up on paperwork and telephone calls.

Chapter Eleven

A day in the life of a veterinary nurse

HANNA is one of the nurses working at the New Millennium Veterinary Practice. She is 21 years old and has worked there since leaving school at 16. She is one of a team of two qualified and two trainee nurses who support the vets, mainly on the small animal side, but occasionally working with horses when they are admitted to the clinic for investigations or treatment.

Hanna's family always kept pets and has been clients of the practice for many years. Hanna was always "animal-mad" and desperately wanted to have a career involving animals. When she was 13 she started working at the surgery on Saturday mornings as a general "dogsbody". Her duties at that time mainly involved cleaning kennels, stacking shelves and mopping floors, but she was happy to be getting experience in a work environment.

She took her GCSEs at 16 and very fortunately there was an opening at New Millennium for a trainee nurse at that time. Hanna signed up and started her two-year training course. She had to travel once a week to the local agricultural college for formal tuition, but most of her training was undertaken within the practice. She passed her exams with flying colours and proudly became a Registered Veterinary Nurse.

Hanna's working day starts at 8.00 am when the surgery opens. Her first job is to attend to any in-patients. These must be checked, their bedding changed, kennels cleaned and given food and water (unless they are scheduled to have an anaesthetic later in the day). Dogs will need to be put out one-at-a-time into the exercise yard. Each animal has a set of clinical notes with it and Hanna has to take and record its morning temperature, note any urine or faeces passed, as well as any vomit or diarrhoea, how much food and water has been taken and keep a note of all medicines given. She then discusses each animal's needs for the day with Ruth, the vet who is in charge of the in-patients.

Some (but not all) dogs and cats may become quite stressed when kept in a strange environment, away from their home-comforts and veterinary nurses spend time trying to reassure the in-patients, to get them more relaxed. Stressed animals can react in unpredictable ways and fear and aggression often go hand-in-hand. Furthermore if an animal is very stressed it will not behave normally, for example by refusing to eat. This makes assessment of its response to treatment more difficult. A nice relaxed patient is therefore safer for everyone and easier to monitor.

A number of animals are booked in each day for routine operations. These are checked by a vet and then admitted to the clinic. Hanna will weigh each one carefully, as anaesthetic doses are all given strictly according to the animal's weight. A pre-med injection of sedative and painkiller is given to each patient about an hour before its anaesthetic. This relaxes the animal, makes it easier to handle and means that less anaesthetic will need to be given.

A pre-anaesthetic blood sample is often taken before surgery: usually in older animals or those that have other health problems. Today a 10 year-old terrier has been booked in for dental work and Hanna and Sue one of the trainee nurses take a blood sample from him. Hanna takes the sample to the practice laboratory and runs it through the analysing machines. Modern lab machines are easy to use and the results come through in around 10 minutes. The tests show that the terrier has a mild kidney problem and so Ruth and Hanna put him on an intra-venous saline drip, which will help him cope better with the anaesthetic.

Routine operations begin as soon as the pre-med injections have had time to work. Today's list starts with a couple of female cats to be spayed. This is a routine procedure, but is still a major internal operation, performed under a general anaesthetic.

Cats are not always the easiest patients and it is important to keep them calm at all times. A cat that becomes stressed and angry can be very difficult to deal with, not to say dangerous, as the claws and teeth can inflict serious damage.

Hanna holds the first cat, gently but firmly, whilst Ruth clips a small area of hair on a front leg and then injects the anaesthetic solution into the vein. Once the cat is asleep a plastic tube is inserted down its windpipe. The tube is then connected to the anaesthetic machine to provide a flow of oxygen and anaesthetic gas to keep the patient sleep for as long as necessary.

It is Hanna's responsibility to monitor the anaesthetic at all times and she keeps a chart where she records the cat's pulse and respiratory rate as well as carefully monitoring the depth of anaesthesia every few minutes.

Whilst the surgeon scrubs up, Hanna prepares the cat for surgery. A small patch of fur on the left flank is clipped and then the skin is carefully and methodically cleaned with surgical disinfectant. The cat is then carried through to the operating theatre. Hanna has already laid out packs of sterile instruments, drapes and suture materials and she then helps Ruth to put on a sterile operating gown and gloves.

The operation takes about 20 minutes and involves removing the uterus and both ovaries through a small incision in the flank. The wound is stitched and when the surgeon is happy with everything Hanna allows the cat to wake up, by stopping the anaesthetic gas, whilst maintaining a flow of oxygen. Just as the cat regains consciousness Hanna removes the breathing tube from the windpipe and then she carefully monitors it to ensure that it continues to breathe well. When she is happy that everything is fine she takes the cat back to its kennel where it is wrapped in a blanket to keep warm.

The operating table then has to be cleared and cleaned ready for the next procedure. Used surgical instruments are scrubbed thoroughly and then packed in bags and re-sterilised in the autoclave (a glorified pressure-cooker) to be ready for another operation.

The morning's operations proceed uneventfully. The terrier needing dental attention is anaesthetised in the treatment room and then Ruth checks its mouth closely. There is a lot of plaque on all the teeth, which Hanna first cleans off, using an ultra-sonic descaler, exactly the same as the one used by a human dental-hygienist. Some of the teeth look diseased, so Ruth then checks each one carefully and decides to remove several which have become loose. Finally the remaining teeth are polished to ensure the surfaces are smooth.

When Hanna hands the dog back to his owner later in the day she will talk about the importance of on-going dental care and try and encourage the owner to start brushing the dog's teeth on a regular basis, to try and prevent the accumulation of more plaque.

Once all the operations are finished Hanna and the trainee nurse will give the operating room a thorough clean before taking a lunch break.

In the afternoon Hanna runs a clinic for overweight dogs and cats. Obesity in pets is becoming a major problem, just as it is for many of their owners. Obese animals can be prone to a variety of ailments, including heart disease, arthritis and diabetes.

Hanna weighs each animal on arrival and discusses what sort of diet it has been on. There is a range of special low-calorie dog and cat foods that she can recommend to the owner to start the slow process of weight-reduction. Owners have to be educated not to allow their pets to get extra treats or titbits, which would defeat the object of the special diet. Many owners feel that they are being unkind by restricting their pet's food, but Hanna impresses on them the health benefits that will result. She often finds it awkward talking about a pet's obese state, when clearly the owner is very much the same: diplomacy is essential!

The rest of Hanna's day is spent attending to the in-patients and later in the afternoon discharging the routine operations. She will see each owner in turn and explain exactly what has been done to the pet. She tells the owner how to look after the patient, that evening in particular and goes through any special care or medicines it needs. She makes sure the owner knows when the animal must come back for a check up or to have its stitches removed.

After a last clean up of the kennel area Hanna heads wearily for home.

Chapter Twelve

A case that needed specialist treatment

Scruffy

THE following is a fictional account of how Scruffy, a dog with a complex medical problem, was referred by Alison at the New Millennium practice to the nearby referral centre, where as a result of the skill of specialists, she was successfully treated:

Mrs Smith took her 6 month-old Yorkshire terrier, Scruffy, to see Alison, who had met her previously when she came in for her vaccinations as a pup. At that time she had seemed a fine healthy specimen.

In recent weeks Mrs Smith had become increasingly concerned about Scruffy. She did not seem to be growing as well as she should and in fact now looked very thin. She had then started behaving oddly and having "funny turns" a couple of times a day.

Alison welcomed Mrs Smith into her consulting room and lifted Scruffy onto the examination table. After a few brief words of chat she started to take a detailed clinical history, trying to get Mrs Smith to express all her concerns. Her heart rather sank when she heard the expression "funny turn", a term much favoured by owners, as this can cover a multitude of clinical problems. Various brain diseases, heart problems, liver disease, and a host of other metabolic diseases can all produce a so-called "funny turn". Trying to gain more information Alison asked Mrs Smith to describe exactly what happened during these episodes and if there was any pattern as to when they occurred. Mrs Smith said Scruffy would become restless and then seem to wander round in a daze, sometimes pressing her head against the wall. She said this often happened twice a day. Alison asked whether it was related to feeding and after a bit of thought Mrs Smith said she now realised that they generally happened an hour or so after Scruffy's morning and evening meal.

Alison then made a full clinical examination of Scruffy as described earlier. This provided very little additional information, other than confirming that Scruffy was indeed very thin and underweight, at 3.5 kg.

Fortunately Alison already had a reasonable idea as to what the problem was. She explained to Mrs Smith that there is a rare congenital problem, particularly seen in Yorkshire terriers and other small breeds, which almost exactly matched Scruffy's symptoms. The condition is called "porto-caval shunt" and arises due to a defect in the blood vessels that run between the gut and the liver. In a normal animal blood from the intestines passes directly to the liver, where all the nutrients and other chemicals absorbed from the bowel are processed and if necessary detoxified. In animals suffering from a shunt, the blood from the gut does not go to the liver, but instead passes directly into the main blood circulation. This causes all sorts of problems as the body is not then receiving properly processed nutrients and some of the toxic chemicals absorbed from the bowel can cause bizarre effects on the brain. This explains why the "funny turns" tend to happen shortly after a meal.

Alison explained that this is a complex and serious disease and of course that her suspicions would have to be confirmed by further tests. However the good news was that in some cases the problem could be successfully treated, either medically or by surgery, although this was rather complicated and would only be undertaken by a specialist.

She explained that she could run some preliminary blood tests, which might lend more weight to her provisional diagnosis, but then Scruffy would need to be referred to a specialist centre. Fortunately there was a very good referral hospital no more than 20 miles away, which had a team of clinicians who could give Scruffy her best chance. She was greatly relieved when Mrs Smith confirmed that she had taken out an insurance policy on Scruffy when she bought her, as the cost of investigating and treating this problem was likely to run to several thousand pounds.

Alison took a blood sample from Scruffy and put it through the practice lab. Several of the results strongly suggested that her diagnosis was correct. She 'phoned the referral centre and made an appointment for the following day.

Mrs Smith took Scruffy to the referral hospital, where she was initially seen by Kate, a specialist in internal medicine. Kate asked Mrs Smith to repeat her story and then also examined Scruffy carefully. She agreed that Alison's diagnosis was almost certainly correct, but said that she would like to do further blood tests, plus some X-rays and an ultrasound of the abdomen to throw more light on the exact nature of the problem.

Scruffy was admitted to the hospital and more blood tests were performed, which added further weight to the diagnosis. Andrew, the diagnostic imaging specialist at the hospital, then took an X-ray of Scruffy's abdomen. This showed that the liver appeared smaller than normal and the kidneys rather too big, which also supported the diagnosis of a shunt. An ultrasound examination of the abdomen was then performed, paying particular attention to the liver and its associated blood vessels. This type of examination requires a very sophisticated machine and great experience on the part of the clinician. Andrew was able to confirm that there was indeed an aberrant blood vessel leading from the bowel directly to the main vein that carries blood back to the heart and that the liver was being totally by-passed. The diagnosis was thus clinched.

A discussion was then held between the various specialists, including Darren the surgeon, to decide on the best way forward and it was agreed that surgery was likely to give a good result. Darren had had plenty of experience operating on dogs with shunts and was quite happy to go ahead with an operation. During the surgery special X-rays are taken of the blood vessels draining the intestines, in order to identify the aberrant vessel, which must then be carefully closed off. This is a complicated procedure and certainly not without risk to the patient.

Mrs Smith was fully advised of all the findings and agreed to let Scruffy go ahead with surgery.

Anaesthesia for dogs with this condition is also more hazardous than normal, as the patient is usually small, underweight and has abnormal liver function. Roger the anaesthetic specialist made a clinical examination of Scruffy so that he could plan his part in the procedure. He decided to put Scruffy on some medical treatment for a few weeks to improve her condition prior to the operation and reduce the anaesthetic risks.

Scruffy was sent home on treatment and then came back for surgery at a later date. Fortunately this went well, without any unexpected problems. Scruffy stayed at the hospital for a further week and than went home to a delighted Mrs Smith.

The insurance company picked up the bill for £3,500!

Chapter Thirteen
The future

THE future of the veterinary profession is secure. Mankind will always have a need for animals.

The ever-increasing human population will have to be fed and although there may be cheaper and more environmentally-friendly ways of doing this, it is unlikely that our desire to consume meat, eggs and milk is going to diminish. The increased potential for serious disease and welfare problems to occur as livestock production intensifies worldwide is going to be a very serious issue.

There is a major role to be played by the veterinary profession in ensuring the health and well-being of livestock, particularly in developing countries, where intensive production has not previously been practised. National and international disease surveillance will be necessary to identify and control disease outbreaks before they can spread and cause economic disaster. Education of a new generation of livestock keepers will be vital.

Farm animal practice in the UK has declined in recent years. However it is likely that increasing demand for food and in particular, meat, in the emerging economies of the world will mean that the UK will have to produce more home-grown food and this will surely include produce derived from animals. It is therefore likely that there will be an increased need for vets to work in the agricultural sector in years to come.

The risk of diseases transmissible from animals to humans, such as mutations of animal flu viruses will be a very big concern as livestock production increases and intensifies. Vets must be constantly on the outlook for these diseases, which may present in new or previously unrecognised forms. The ability of people to travel so easily and quickly around the world means that an outbreak of a new variant of a flu virus in some obscure third world country cannot just be treated as a local problem. Within a very short time it could spread across the planet.

Somewhat ironically it has been pointed out that the increasing numbers of livestock will also contribute significantly to global warming (if it happens) as a result of the methane released from their collective digestive tracts. In turn, increased global warming would lead to the spread of many diseases transmitted by insects or other parasites to areas of the world where they did not previously occur. Numerous diseases are spread in this way in tropical and sub-tropical areas of the world. It is likely that those of us living in temperate areas will have to face up to the reality of new diseases affecting both ourselves and our animals. New vaccines and anti-parasitic drugs will be needed.

At the other end of the scale, small animal practice in the UK must also have a secure future, as it is unlikely that the human-companion animal bond is going to suddenly disappear. There are however some real concerns about the economics of small animal practice as it currently stands. Changes in society can have a major effect on the type and numbers of pets that people keep. For example, it is thought that the number of dogs in the UK has declined in recent years. This is easily explained if one considers the radical changes in family life in the last 30 years or so.

The traditional family, consisting of a married couple with children, where the husband went out to work, whilst the wife stayed at home, is largely a thing of the past. The majority of women now also go out to work, leaving the home empty for much of the day. A dog, which requires regular access to the outdoors for exercise and to perform its bodily functions, may no longer be a convenient pet for this type of household. Cats, which are easily trained to use a litter-tray or can come and go freely through a cat-flap, may be far more appropriate. It is thought that cat numbers have risen as those of dogs have fallen, although a recent survey suggests there are still more dogs than cats in the UK. Rabbits have also grown in popularity as house pets, (rather than the traditional children's pet, kept in a hutch in the garden) for the same reason, being easy to manage and house-trainable. Economic pressures may also mean that families keep fewer pets than before.

These changes in pet ownership have a significant effect on veterinary practices. Dogs generate more income for vets than cats, whilst rabbits lag even further behind. Practice incomes have levelled off, or even diminished, in the past few years. Client numbers per practice have declined and vets are finding that they have to try and generate more income from a smaller pool of clients. In addition, particularly in urban and suburban areas, there has been a proliferation in practice numbers, leading to fierce competition and price-cutting in some cases. Consumers might regard this as a good thing, but in the long term all businesses need to be profitable in order to invest for the future.

Most vets strongly encourage their clients to take out insurance for their pets, as this works to the benefit of both the pet and the vet. Without financial restrictions on treatment obviously the vet can offer far more, without the fear of an unpaid bill at the end of the treatment. Unfortunately, as veterinary charges have escalated in recent years (well ahead of retail inflation) so the cost of insuring animals has also risen. There is concern that pet insurance could price itself out of the market. This would clearly have a very negative impact on practices in general and referral practices in particular.

As veterinary fees escalate there will undoubtedly be an increasing need for charities such as the RSPCA, PDSA and Blue Cross to provide veterinary care for those owners who cannot afford to use private practices. The subject of charities providing free veterinary care to the less well-off in society raises some interesting questions. Owning an animal is after all a lifestyle choice and not a necessity. No one would seriously expect a charity to pay for example for the repair of that same person's TV or home computer. The counter argument is that animal welfare considerations dictate that an unfortunate pet should not suffer just because the owner is impoverished.

There has been a growth in corporate and joint-venture practices in recent years, at the expense of traditional partnerships. Some of the pioneers in this area talked of transforming the veterinary profession in the same way that the nation's opticians were turned upside-down in the 1980s and '90s. Opticians formerly made up a very fragmented profession, with many practices owned by private individuals or small partnerships, operating from high street shops or private houses. Compare that with the present situation, where the profession is dominated by a small handful of nationwide chains, whose brands are a feature of every high street. To date this has not happened with the veterinary profession and it is probably unlikely to do so, for a variety of reasons.

Oddly enough, one of the major requirements for a successful veterinary practice is good parking facilities for clients. This often precludes the establishment of practices on the high street, where corporate practices would ideally like to be, so as to be highly visible to the public (as are the opticians). Veterinary premises also need a lot more space than opticians if they are going to offer anything more than a basic service and again this limits the use of small high street shop units. Although there are of course practices based in small units, these may not offer an attractive career option to young graduates, because of the limited facilities and services they can offer. Some practices have moved into out-of-town retail parks, but again space may be limited here and they do not always offer a particularly attractive work environment for a professional person. Rental costs may also be expensive, as they will be competing with major and financially-powerful retailers.

It is likely that the traditional partnership model will survive, although high levels of student debt and the ever increasing value of property can make it more difficult for young vets to buy into established businesses.

It was feared at one time (by the old-guard) that the dominance of the profession by women in recent years would have a profound effect on life in veterinary practice. Most people now agree that this has not happened. There will be an increasing demand for part-time work by women with commitments to their families, but there is no reason why practices cannot adapt to this. Young vets generally demand a better work-life balance than their predecessors and no longer want to be endlessly on-call at night and weekends. European Working Time Regulations now preclude this. There has been a rapid development of dedicated out-of-hours clinics in recent years and this is likely to continue. The downside of this is that many young vets will never experience some of the more exciting emergency problems affecting their patients, which for various reasons tend to happen at night.

The rise in referral practices has changed life for the general practitioner. Today there is easy-access to top-class specialists and in many cases it may be considered unethical to attempt a procedure when someone else nearby can clearly do it better. The ever-present fear of litigation by a disgruntled client certainly makes many vets feel that they should refer animals to a specialist rather than tackle the problem themselves. The result is that many veterinary GPs now act more like their human counterparts, filtering out anything serious, which they then refer to the specialist and only dealing with relatively straight forward problems themselves.

It has to be asked whether this type of general practice is going to offer an attractive career option to the academically high-flyers coming out of the veterinary schools. There is a limit to the number of specialists that the profession can support and there will not be unlimited opportunities for young graduates down that route.

The business model for lavishly-equipped referral centres is dependent upon there being a suitable population of pets which are either insured, or owned by those with the financial means to pay substantial fees. Questions are beginning to be asked as to how sustainable these centres will be, particularly if pet insurance became too expensive for many owners.

Increased affluence and leisure time have lead to an increase in horses kept for sporting and recreational purposes. People have always had a fascination with and love of horses, which is unlikely to disappear. Equine practice seems to have a good future. There has however been an increase in the number of practices dedicated to equine work and in some areas competition between them is fierce.

Medical science and technology have progressed at a prodigious rate since the middle of the 20th century and veterinary medicine has benefited from many of these advances to an extraordinary degree. Surely no one would have foreseen 20 years ago that such high-tech wonders as CT and MRI scanning would be readily available for animal use, or that dogs could have replacement joints, whilst those with cancer would be undergoing advanced chemo- and radio-therapy.

There is a question as to how far medical treatment of animals should go. Is animal life as important as human life? Should we treat animals to the absolute limits of our abilities?

Western culture supports the view that human life is sacrosanct and that medical support should never be withdrawn, other than under the most exceptional circumstances. Should this philosophy extend equally to our pets?

Many vets would argue that "quality of life" is more important than just "life" itself, but there is a risk that some may get so carried away with their ability to prolong life, using advanced high-tech medicine, that they lose sight of common sense. Equally, some owners will insist that "everything that can be done, must be done" to prolong the life of a cherished pet, regardless of cost, or the animal's best interests.

Euthanasia of humans is forbidden in the UK, forcing some desperate and terminally-ill patients to travel to so-called "euthanasia clinics" which are allowed to operate legally in other countries. However, there appears to be increasing public support for at least debating this issue. Indeed recent surveys indicate that a substantial number of people feel that we should have the right to choose the time of our own demise.

Vets, on the other hand, have the legal right to terminate the life of an animal, but are increasingly under pressure from owners to make use of all the advances in medical science to keep a beloved pet going to the bitter end.

As they say, "It's a funny old world …"

Where to find out more

www.rcvs.org.uk Royal College of Veterinary Surgeons

www.bva.co.uk British Veterinary Association

www.bvna.org.uk British Veterinary Nursing Association

www.noah.co.uk National Office of Animal Health

www.vmd.gov.uk Veterinary Medicines Directorate

www.defra.gov.uk Department for the Environment, Food & Rural Affairs (DEFRA)

www.rspca.org.uk RSPCA

www.bluecross.org.uk Blue Cross

www.pdsa.org.uk PDS

www.the-kennel-club.org.uk The Kennel Club

www.bhs.org.uk British Horse Society

www.nfuonline.com National Farmers' Union

www.battersea.org.uk Battersea Dogs' Home

www.dogstrust.org.uk The Dogs' Trust

www.fabcats.org Feline Advisory Bureau

www.aht.org.uk The Animal Health Trust

About the author

BOB LEHNER has worked with everything from hamsters to horses, as well as having had experience in the pharmaceuticals industry, commercial deer farming and zoo animals.

Bob was born and brought up in Kenya, coming to the UK in 1969 to study veterinary medicine at Edinburgh University.

After qualifying, he remained in Edinburgh and gained a PhD in parasite immunology. He then went into veterinary practice, where he spent most of his career as a partner in a multi-vet, mixed, hospital-based practice in Hertfordshire.

He retired from his position as senior partner in 2005, but continues to work part time in practice. He is also an inspector for the RCVS Practice Standards Scheme, which helps to regulate the profession.

Since retiring he has also worked with an animal charity in Botswana, neutering feral dogs.

Bob lives in Hertfordshire, where he and his wife share their lives with a horse, a dog, three cats and a house-rabbit.

More titles in the Quicklook series

You can find out more about our wide range of titles at **quicklookbooks.com**

Quicklook at Police

The British police have pioneered many aspects of policing. We explore how and why and how the service is shaping up to the 21st century. We find out about the many different skills and departments and how they fit together.

Quicklook at Pensions

This clear, layman friendly, book is a must read for anyone looking for a "spin free" guide to pensions.

Quicklook at Management

Every organisation needs to be managed. Part art, part science, part seat of the pants, there are many approaches. This up to date book covers the main ideas.

Quicklook at Education

This guide to the vital subject of education covers the system from pre-school to post graduate, exams and qualifications, the teaching professions and theories of learning.

Quicklook at Movies

This brings the world of film to life as we explore the characters that shaped and starred in it, the technology which developed it, the many different types of film and the booms and busts of an industry sometimes as dramatic as anything on screen.

Quicklook at Business

This is the most comprehensive short guide to the business world that you are likely to find.

Quicklook at Marketing

Marketing affects us all. It is crucial to business success. What is it and how does it work? Experienced marketing expert Patrick Forsyth unwraps its mysteries. You launch a new product.

Quicklook at Defence

Defence is vital and often in the news. How does it operate in a time of new challenges and tight budgets? Command a crisis operation.

Quicklook at Human Resources

This is a must for anyone interested in a job or the world of work.

Quicklook at Accountancy

All of the basics are covered, from the key elements of accounts and the ways in which they are used. Accountancy is the backbone of most organisations. It is itself a huge industry. We look at the main players, how it works and the many career options.

Quicklook at India

An emerging superpower, India embraces many different peoples, languages and religions. Nowhere has older or deeper cultures, or so much diversity.

Quicklook at Dogs

There are over seven million dog owners in the UK. Find out why we share such a strong bond with our canine companions.

Quicklook at Wine

Wine is a luxury enjoyed by many, but understood by few. This book gets you to grips with the subject, from grapes to glass.

Quicklook at Vets

Millions of us care for animals and vets are familiar and reassuring figures. Find out about the tremendous scope of their work.

Quicklook at Flying

How has flying developed? How does a plane work? What is happening in aviation now? What will happen in the future? What does it take to be a pilot?

Quicklook at Property

Property (real estate) is the ultimate base for wealth and the economy. It comes in many forms. Many jobs depend on it. Learn how the world of property operates.

Quicklook at Medicine

Medicine provides more and more remedies, often vital to life. What is becoming possible? How is it done? How does the body work? Find out about the medical professions. Be a GP for a day.

Quicklook at Law

English Law has spread its influence to many countries. Why? How does it work? How is it changing? How does the legal profession operate? Get inside a Court case.